PREPARATION OF
SCIENTIFIC AND TECHNICAL
PAPERS

PREPARATION OF
SCIENTIFIC *and* TECHNICAL
PAPERS

BY

SAM F. TRELEASE
Associate Professor of Botany in Columbia University

AND

EMMA SAREPTA YULE
*Head, Department of English in the College of Agriculture of the
University of the Philippines*

THE WILLIAMS & WILKINS COMPANY
BALTIMORE, U. S. A.
1927

Composed and Printed at the
WAVERLY PRESS
for
The Williams & Wilkins Company
Baltimore, Md., U. S. A.

CONTENTS

6 CONTENTS

PREFACE

This manual is intended for the use of students who are writing articles on scientific or technical subjects. It is designed primarily as a reference book for senior and graduate students who want information concerning matters of style to be followed in the preparation of papers.

We hope that the student who is confronted with the arduous task of "writing up" his data will find in this book many suggestions that will not only lighten his work, but enable him to present his material in a more effective form. As the writing of theses usually is postponed until very late, this guide as to style and manner of presentation should be a convenient aid.

This handbook is not a manufactured product, not a collection of theories; it grew. The suggestions and directions it contains were originally prepared to aid students in writing themes and theses at the College of Agriculture of the University of the Philippines. The aim was to include only material that would be especially useful to senior students preparing theses for publication in *The Philippine Agriculturist*, published by the College. The suggestions were first used in mimeographed form; they were published five years ago in a pamphlet with the title *The Preparation of Theses and Other Manuscripts*. The pamphlet was adopted by the College of Agriculture as the guide in matters of form to be used in College publications; it is used as a supplementary textbook in teaching theme writing in the English courses at the College.

The unqualified appreciation of the manual shown by faculty and students of the College of Agriculture has led us to prepare the present handbook, *Preparation of Scientific and Technical Papers*. We hope that it may be of service to students in other colleges. A thorough revision has been made of the original text. Also, many changes have been made to bring various points of style into conformity with that of the Waverly Press of Baltimore, Md., a publishing house that has developed a high standard in scientific and technical publications.

Although, in the main, the directions given are for the preparation of a thesis or dissertation, they apply to the writing of reports in science, agriculture, engineering, and medicine, and to the preparing of manuscript of a more popular nature on a scientific or technical subject. The process is essentially the same whatever the use to be made of the product.

In recording the results of laboratory experiments, the student has abundant opportunity for acquiring skill in writing. To make rapid improvement, he should apply the knowledge he has gained in the study of English composition and frequently consult a handbook that deals specifically with scientific writing. The practical value of this work will be increased if each report is revised carefully and then rewritten. Daily practice is the most important factor in acquiring skill in writing.

Many of the rules given in this book are based upon recognized authorities, listed in the bibliography at the end of this volume. In selecting the rules and in making the suggestions, we have been guided by a number of years of experience in reading student manuscripts and journal copy. Some of the directions are given to secure uniformity. Two or more ways may be approved by usage, but it is convenient to adopt one form. Nevertheless, individuality should be encouraged if accuracy and conciseness are retained.

No attempt has been made to include rules of grammar and rhetoric. These subjects are treated in so many handbooks and textbooks of English composition that their inclusion here would be superfluous. It is taken for granted that the student will have on his desk a good handbook of composition, a copy of *Roget's Thesaurus*, and an authoritative dictionary—a large abridgment, at least, of *Webster's New International Dictionary*.

In general, the style herein suggested conforms to the standard style of the Waverly Press, and we are glad to acknowledge valuable help from Mr. Grover C. Orth, editor. We are indebted to Mr. Orth for preparing the manuscript of the sections on tables, abbreviations, and styles of type, as well as for many important revisions in other parts of the handbook.

We wish to acknowledge valuable suggestions from Prof. E. D. Hester and Prof. L. B. Uichanco, of the University of the Philippines, from Mr. Richard C. MacGregor, of the Philippine Bureau of Science, and from Dr. J. Mattern, of the Johns Hopkins University. We are indebted especially to Mr. C. C. Barton, of the U. S. Department of Commerce, Dr. W. J. Humphreys, of the U. S. Weather Bureau, and Mr. C. Bowyer Vaux, of the Wistar Institute, who have kindly read and criticized the manuscript. It is a pleasure to express our gratitude to Prof. William Trelease, of the University of Illinois, and Prof. Burton E. Livingston, of the Johns Hopkins University, for advice and criticism upon which many of the suggestions have been based. Our sincere thanks are due also to Mrs. Helen M. Trelease, who has given valuable help during the revisions of the manuscript.

August 29, 1927.

FIRST STEPS IN TREATING SCIENTIFIC DATA

1. *Calculations.* Check all calculations, and put experimental data in the form of tables. Make all calculations twice, preferably on different days, and, if practicable, in different ways. The second calculation should be made without reference to the first, and on a new page in your notebook. Notes on observational and descriptive work should be arranged and classified.

2. *Graphs.* Plot your data wherever possible. In most experimentation, graphs furnish the best means of bringing out relations between data, and should be prepared to aid in interpretation even if they are not to be published.

3. *Conclusions.* Examine the tables, graphs, and classified notes for conclusions and relations. Ask yourself, "What is the true explanation of the facts?" If several explanations seem equally probable, do not emphasize *one.* Consider all logical possibilities. Make written notes of tentative conclusions. If time is available, verify your conclusions by gathering more data or by making special test experiments. Estimate the probable accuracy of your results by considering the sources of error.[1] Conclusions from your results must be based upon a careful consideration of their accuracy and suf-

[1]Student: The probable error of a mean. Biometrika, 1908, vi, 1–25.

Pearl, Raymond: Medical biometry and statistics. 1923. 379 p., 71 fig. Philadelphia: W. B. Saunders Company.

Davenport, C. B.: Statistical methods. 1904. 2nd ed., viii + 223 p. New York: John Wiley & Sons.

Yule, G. U.: An introduction to the theory of statistics. 1924. 7th ed., xv + 415 p., 53 fig. London: C. Griffin and Company.

ficiency. If you have enough data, calculate the *probable error* of each of your means.

4. *Revision of conclusions.* Refer again to your data to see whether your tentative conclusions actually are justified. Discover in which cases these conclusions apply and in which, if any, they do not. Modify, if necessary, the statement of your conclusions, and see whether they are consistent with known facts pertaining to the same subject.

5. *Exceptions.* Examine the data for exceptions, inconsistencies, discrepancies, and anomalies. Record the exceptions, and check their values. Some of the most important scientific discoveries have been made because of apparent exceptions and abnormalities in data.

Formulate plausible explanations for the exceptions.

Study your conclusions again to see how the exceptions modify them.

6. *Written notes.* Record on paper any ideas that occur to you; do not crowd your notes. The mechanical process of preparing a paper is a matter of mere detail, subject to endless variation. Some writers like to use a standard size of cards (3 by 5 inches, or 5 by 8) for all preliminary work on a paper. The cards may be filed in a box, under appropriate headings. Only one topic is put on a card, and this topic is expanded later to make a paragraph. This method allows topics to be added, eliminated, and rearranged, whenever necessary. Other writers prefer to use sheets of paper of standard size ($8\frac{1}{2}$ by 11 inches being used almost universally), placing only one topic on a sheet and filing the sheets in folders, large envelopes, or loose-leaf notebooks. (Original observations and measurements usually are recorded in a notebook with permanent pages. A copy should be put in a safe place as soon as possible.)

PUTTING YOUR IDEAS ON PAPER

1. *Mechanical process.* There probably is no best way to prepare a scientific paper, except as may be determined by the individual writer and the circumstances. With no notes at all, one may start writing an article which, short or long, is practically finished at every stage; or one may accumulate the facts in a great mass of verbiage, and then compress the paper to the required limit. It is the end product that counts, not the intermediate steps.

2. *Preliminary outlines.* Many writers obtain best results by developing a preliminary outline before they start writing. The following steps may be employed: (*a*) Prepare a brief outline of your article. This outline may be one or two pages in length. (*b*) Make a second, enlarged outline. This may be three or four times as long as the first. (*c*) Prepare a third outline before beginning the actual writing. In this outline each topic should be enlarged, and the topics should be shifted to the most effective order. (*d*) Begin the actual writing.

PLAN AND ORDER OF TOPICS

1. *Nature of scientific writing.* An article on a scientific or technical subject necessarily contains (*a*) a report of facts, (*b*) an interpretation of facts, or (*c*) a combination of a report and an interpretation. The method of writing should, of course, be governed by many conditions, such as the purposes of the article, the nature of the subject, the characteristics of the writer and the probable reader, etc. Obviously, no set method or arrangement will be suited to all kinds of articles. It is important, however, that the plan of the composition be very clear to the reader. The main topics and their subdivisions should

be clearly shown. In this respect scientific writing differs somewhat from literary writing. A scientific article is intended to be studied and used as a reference; it is not merely to be read. Hence, literary devices should be subordinated if they interfere with clearness. The plan should be self-evident throughout the composition.

2. *General outline.* The outline given below is only suggestive. An examination of many articles published in scientific journals will show that the majority of them have this general arrangement and sequence of topics. This form of outline is well adapted to most scientific articles that report investigations or experiments, and possesses the additional advantage of being familiar to the reader. The outline should be modified sufficiently to fulfill the special requirements of a particular article.

General outline of a scientific article

I. *Title.* The title should consist preferably of few words, indicative of the contents that are most emphasized. Great care must be exercised to employ words that contain the elements both of brevity and comprehensiveness and permit of easy and accurate indexing.

II. *Introduction.* (*a*) Nature of problem; scope; bearing; importance.

    (*b*) Review of the important literature on the subject.

    (*c*) Object of work.

    (*d*) Time and place of work.

III. *Materials and methods.* (*a*) Description of the equipment and materials employed.

    (*b*) Explanation of the way in which the work was done. Emphasize the features that are new.

IV. *Experiments and results.*[2]   (*a*) Detailed description of the experiments.

   (*b*) Description of the results. If possible, these should be shown in tables and plotted as graphs.

V. *Discussion of results.*[3]   (*a*) Main principles, causal relations, or generalizations that are shown by the results. Choose one or several main points which you wish to prove.

   (*b*) Evidence (as shown by the data) for each of these main points.

   (*c*) Exceptions and opposing theories, and explanations of these.

   (*d*) Comparison of your results and interpretations with those of other workers. (See also section 11, p. 19.)

VI. *Summary.* A condensed account of the important contents, in a form suited to the requirements of abstract journals.

3. *Special outlines.* The following outlines, modified to suit the particular investigations, have been found satisfactory.

Outline of a laboratory report

I. *Title.*

II. *Object.*

III. *Equipment.* Apparatus and materials, diagram of apparatus.

IV. *Method.* Experimental procedure or manipulations.

[2] The results may be compared to "news" in a daily paper.
[3] The discussion of results may be compared to an editorial in a daily paper, and contains an interpretation of data.

    V. *Results*. Observations and data, calculations, tables, graphs.

   VI. *Conclusions*. Interpretation of observations and results.

Outline of an article on disease in plants

      I. *Title*.
     II. *Introduction*.
    III. *The disease*.
    IV. *The causal organism*.
     V. *Life history of the causal organism in relation to the disease*.
   VI. *Methods of control*.
  VII. *Discussion of results*.
VIII. *Summary*.

Outline of an article on disease in man

      I. *Title*.
     II. *Introduction*.
    III. *Etiology*.
    IV. *Pathology*.
     V. *Symptoms*.
   VI. *Diagnosis*.
  VII. *Complications and sequels*.
VIII. *Prognosis*.
   IX. *Prevention and treatment*.
    X. *Discussion of results*.
   XI. *Summary*.

Outline of an engineering report

      I. *Title*.
     II. *Summary*. Condensed account of object of work, significant results, general conclusions, and specific recommendations.

III. *Introduction*. Definition of problem, object of investigation.

IV. *Apparatus and materials*.

V. *Method*. Procedure and processes.

VI. *Results*. Tabulations, graphs, and description.

VII. *Discussion of results*. Explanation and significance of results, together with evidence shown by data.

VIII. *Appendices*. Calculations, technical data.

GENERAL SUGGESTIONS ON SUBJECT MATTER AND ARRANGEMENT

TITLE

1. *Choice of title*. Choose a concise descriptive title, complete enough to give the main topics needed for making a subject index in an abstract journal or for a library. Select these topics with the aim of giving definite ideas as to the exact contents of your article. In a biological study, the name of the organism should appear in the title. If necessary, sacrifice brevity in order to include all important nouns under which your article should be indexed. Place the more important words near the beginning of the title.

2. *Selection of topics*. Ask yourself, "Under what topics would I naturally look in a subject index of an abstract journal if I were searching for the literature on the subjects treated in my article?" The answer to this question will provide the topics which you should include in your title.

DISCUSSION OF RESULTS

3. *Unity*. An article should be a unit, treating a single definite subject. It may contain a number of

main topics if these are logical divisions of one large subject. Each paragraph should have unity; it may contain a topic sentence that summarizes the whole thought of the paragraph. Make a careful selection of materials. Include only what is necessary to an understanding of the main ideas, but omit nothing that is essential.

4. *Orderly arrangement of topics.* Choose a logical sequence of topics, basing this upon relations of space, time, importance, similarity or contrast, complexity, or cause and effect. Choose an order that serves best the needs of clearness, coherence, and emphasis. Discuss similar points in the same order, and use similar forms of expression. Indicate clearly the beginning of each new topic.

5. *Development.* Develop the main ideas until they are so clear that they may be understood easily by one of your fellow students—who, you may assume, is not a specialist in the subject on which you are writing. Try to define, explain, illustrate, prove, and summarize your statements. Explain each topic clearly, point by point. Give considerable thought to the relative importance of the several topics and their need of development. Treat briefly those topics that are too simple to require detailed explanation. Develop fully the more important topics.

6. *Examples.* So far as practicable, illustrate the meaning of every general or abstract statement by giving examples, particular instances, concrete data, amplifying details, and specific comparisons. The best method of explaining abstract ideas is by means of concrete examples.

7. *Answers to reader's questions.* Consider what questions the reader will wish answered in your article.

Answer the questions "Why?" and "How?" Show the meaning of the observed facts, their interrelations, their underlying causes, and their effects. Aim to explain facts in the symbols or language of mathematics, and according to the laws of physics and chemistry.

8. *Words.* Employ words that are approved by good usage. Be careful to avoid those that are obscure, ambiguous, or inappropriate. Try to use words that a foreigner will be able to find in a small dictionary. (For example, a foreigner might not know what you mean if you mention a "tumbler," but he will understand if you add that this is a "cylindrical glass vessel, 5–6 cm. in diameter and about 10 cm. deep.")

9. *Definitions.* Define all technical terms that the reader might not understand.

10. *Tone.* Skill may be developed in presenting material in a tactful way. Clear statements supported by evidence are better than positive assertions. Be careful not to announce a well-known fact as if it were a discovery. Indicate clearly which of your results and conclusions are new. For completeness of discussion, it often is necessary to mention to the reader many things that he knows already; but this may be done skillfully, without annoying the reader or confusing him.

11. *Unsettled points.* Give particular attention to evidence that has a bearing on points concerning which there is a difference of opinion among scientists. But avoid personal or controversial language, or expressions likely to excite controversy or retort.

12. *Topics of general interest.* Develop in detail the topics that are of general interest.

13. *Applications.* Show the practical applications of your study to agriculture, industry, engineering, medicine, etc.

14. *Emphasis of general conclusions.* Indicate the ways in which the results of your study are related to the science as a whole. Emphasize the additions that your study makes to the science, and lay stress upon conclusions that modify in a significant way any laws or principles that have secured general acceptance. Develop with special clearness observations or inferences that seem to you to be of sufficient importance to deserve mention in a textbook on your subject.

15. *Qualification of conclusions.* To prevent misunderstanding, it is necessary to define as clearly as possible the precise conditions which must be fulfilled before your conclusions will be true.

Confusion often results from failure to define adequately all influential experimental details. In any experiment or series of experiments the influential features may be analyzed conveniently into two groups: (1) Those that represent the variables to be specially studied, and (2) those representing the rest of the experimental complex. The influential conditions of the first group are assumed to be adequately known; they are the conditions that are purposely made to differ in certain known ways. For an ideal experiment or experiment series the influential conditions of the second group should be as thoroughly known and definitely described as are the acknowledged variables. The statement of conclusions should be qualified in such a way as to indicate the sets of influential conditions to which the experimental results may be considered as applicable.

16. *Stimulation.* Try to stimulate the reader to further thought and research on the subject of your study.

SUMMARY

17. *Nature.* The summary should be an abstract of the significant contents of the paper. It should state briefly the principal results and conclusions, and should indicate the methods by which these have been reached. It should be comprehensive, but consist mainly of additions (*new* facts or interpretations) which the paper makes to our knowledge. It should be concise and brief; few summaries should contain more than three hundred words.

18. *Models.* Study as models the abstracts given in the abstract journals, and try to make a summary that an abstractor (one who is as well acquainted with the field as you are yourself) will wish to insert, without alteration, in an abstract journal.

19. *Purpose.* In preparing a title and a summary for an article, it is important to realize that the individual worker glances through many more articles than he can possibly have time to read carefully. He is likely to read the title of your article and then, if interested, to turn to your summary for a digest of the contents. *Your summary should tell him at a glance whether or not he should read the article.* He wants a summary that presents accurately the essential contents of an article—the main facts and conclusions. The summary should be self-explanatory, complete and clear in itself, and worded in non-technical language, if possible.

OUTLINES FOR VARIOUS COMPOSITIONS

1. *General.* An outline for an article of a more popular nature should, of course, be much more flexible than the general outline given above. But the same line of development should be followed.

2. *Title.* The title usually should be short—not more

than seven words. It may aim to attract the reader's attention, but it should not be misleading.

3. *Introduction.* The introduction usually should be brief. It is, however, a very important part of any paper. The word "introduction" means "act of leading into"; hence, the statements in this part should lead the reader into the discussion, or body of the article.

4. *Analysis of subject.* Instead of "materials and methods" and "experiments and results," there should be the statement of the question to be discussed. This should be divided into topics and subtopics as the writer presents them in his discussion.

5. *Discussion.* The discussion should follow many of the suggestions given on pages 17 to 20.

6. *Conclusion.* The conclusion should not be so formal as in a technical article, but adapted, of course, to the nature of the discussion or body of the article. It may be (*a*) a summing up of points, (*b*) recommendations, (*c*) combination of (*a*) and (*b*), (*d*) general statements with the purpose of leaving a clear impression in the mind of the reader.

USE OF TENSES IN SCIENTIFIC PAPERS

1. *Experimental facts.* The experimental facts should be given in the *past tense.* (For example: The plants *grew* better in A than in B; the dry weight *was* greater in A than in B.)

2. *Presentation.* The remarks about the presentation of data should be mainly in the *present tense.* (For example: Diagrams showing yields have been drawn and *are* shown in figure 3. The second column of table 2 *represents* the dry weight of tops.)[4]

---

[4] The Government Printing Office capitalizes the words *table* and *figure*.

3. *Discussions of results.* Discussions of results may be in both the *past* and *present tenses*, swinging back and forth from the experimental facts to the presentation, etc. (For example: The highest dry weight *is* shown for culture A, which *received* the greatest amount of the ammonium salt. This may mean that the amount of nitrogen added *was* the determining condition for these experiments.)

4. *Specific conclusions.* Specific conclusions and deductions should be stated in the *past tense*, because this always emphasizes the special conditions of the particular experiments and avoids confusing special conclusions with general ones. (For example: Rice *grew* better, under the other conditions of these tests, when ammonium sulphate *was* added to the soil. Do not say: Rice *grows* better when ammonium sulphate *is* added to the soil.)

5. *General truths.* When a general truth is mentioned, it should, of course, be stated in the *present tense*. Logically, a general truth is without time distinction. For example, one may say, "Many years ago, scientists were convinced that malaria *is* caused by a germ carried by a certain species of mosquito." General conclusions, well-established principles of mathematics, physics, and chemistry, should be put in the *present tense*.

REVISIONS

After writing the first draft of your article, begin to revise it. Revise many times, having one principal object in mind each time. It is not necessary to copy the pages until they become crowded with corrections.

1. *Consistency.* If the article be long, the first part may have to be rewritten to conform to the last part. Avoid contradicting yourself. In this revision you may

rearrange the order of the topics, if necessary. Irrelevant parts should be eliminated. Important parts may be expanded, and minor parts subordinated.

2. *Sentences.* Revise with the object of improving the structure and length of sentences. Few sentences should have more than thirty words. Choose sentence structures that require simple punctuation. Simple sentences lead to clearness.

3. *Clearness.* Revise sentences and paragraphs with special attention to clearness. There should be only one possible meaning. There usually is a best word or phrase to express an idea. Find the best.

4. *Repetition.* Revise to eliminate frequent repetitions of the same sentence structure, or of the same word, particularly if close together and with different meanings.

5. *Connectives.* Revise, giving special attention to connectives.

6. *Euphony.* Revise so that your article reads smoothly aloud.

7. *Punctuation.* Revise with the object of correcting punctuation.

8. *Style.* Revise, paying special attention to consistency in the use of capitals, the use of italics, and the style of headings. Avoid unnecessary use of capitals and italics.

9. *Accuracy.* Finally, read through carefully, searching for inaccuracy or exaggeration of statement.

10. *Length.* As a rule, the first draft of an article should be longer and more complete than the copy that will be offered for publication. Better results usually are obtained by trimming a long article than by expanding a short one. The article may need to be shortened to meet the limit specified by the journal in which it is to be published. In reducing an article, eliminate or condense the parts that are least needed for clear-

ness of presentation. Shorten by leaving out the obvious and the least important. Retain the essentials. Impartial counsel is valuable in aiding you to decide on what is essential. In judging, put yourself in the place of the reader. Be impersonal, a difficult thing when estimating your own work. It takes moral strength to "blue pencil" choice phrases, paragraphs, and ideas. But the results will justify the effort.

A long paper often may be divided into two or more short papers, and these may be published separately. Care should be taken, however, to make each paper a unit, containing one central topic. A paper may treat two or more topics if these logically comprise a single large topic.

PREPARATION OF TYPEWRITTEN COPY

1. *Copy for typist.* Copy for the typist should be clearly written. All of the sheets should be of the same size, and numbered in the upper right-hand corner.

2. *One side of paper.* Write on only one side of the paper.

3. *Flat.* Never roll a manuscript. If possible, keep it flat; but when necessary, it may be folded.

4. *Pins or clips.* The sheets should be fastened together with pins or clips, which can be removed easily.

5. *Typewritten manuscripts.* Typewritten manuscripts must be double-spaced on white paper. Paper of ordinary weight and standard size ($8\frac{1}{2}$ by 11, or 8 by $10\frac{1}{2}$ inches)[5] should be used. At least two typewritten copies should be made, and the author should retain one corrected copy. The original copy (from the ribbon) always should be sent to the publisher, since a carbon copy is easily erased and may become illegible.

[5] The $8\frac{1}{2}$ by 11 inch sheet is the standard of nearly all offices.

6. *Margins.* There should be a blank space of at least 1½ inches (4 cm.) at the top of the first page, 1 inch (2.5 cm.) at the top of the other pages, and 1 inch at the bottom of each page. There should be a blank margin of at least 1¼ inches (3.2 cm.) at the left side of each page and 1 inch at the right side.

7. *Page numbers.* The pages of the typewritten copy should be numbered consecutively in the upper right-hand corner.

8. *Models of style.* The author should make a careful study of a current number of the journal in which his article is to be published, and he should prepare his copy so that it conforms to the prescribed style.

9. *Author's name and address.* The author's name and the address to which proofs are to be sent should be written near the top of the first page of the manuscript. A circle should be drawn around this name and address, to show that it is not to be printed.

10. *Title and name of author.* The title of the article and the author's name should appear on the first page of the manuscript, the first line standing at least 1½ inchs (4 cm.) from the top of the page. The following examples show complete headings that may be modified to suit the style of almost any journal.

[Example of general heading]

GROWTH OF WHEAT SEEDLINGS IN RELATION TO TEMPERATURE[1]

M. R. TOWNSEND AND W. H. MARSHALL

From the Department of Botany, The University of Wisconsin, Madison, Wisconsin

THREE TEXT FIGURES AND TWO PLATES

---

[1] Botanical contribution from The University of Wisconsin, No. 87.

[Example of heading for thesis]

CULTIVATION OF COCONUTS[1]

MANUEL ROXAS

TWO PLATES

---

[1] Thesis presented for graduation from The College of Agriculture, No. ——; Experiment Station contribution, No. ——. Prepared in the Department of ————————, under the direction of Professor ————————.

---

11. *Tables, footnotes, citations, headings, legends.* See special directions for typewriting tables (p. 51), footnotes (p. 60), citations (p. 62), headings (p. 95), legends (p. 106). It is essential that the manuscript be prepared in a way that will allow economical composition on a typesetting machine. The monotype machine can not compose two sizes of type in one operation. To permit rapid work, the manuscript should be arranged so that material to be printed in small type may be separated easily from the text.

Each individual table and each quotation exceeding five lines should be typewritten on a separate sheet of paper; these pages should be numbered consecutively with the text pages.

Footnotes should not be typewritten with the text, but should be put on separate sheets (as many footnotes as convenient being written on a sheet); these should be placed at the end of the text copy, after the bibliography.

The bibliography should begin on a new sheet.

The legends, or titles, of plates and figures should be written in numerical order on one or more sheets, and these should be placed after the footnotes.

12. *Condensed title for running headlines.* A condensed title of 35 letters or less should be given by the

author for the running headlines of the pages. This may be placed on a separate sheet at the end of the manuscript.

CORRECTIONS AND ALTERATIONS IN MANUSCRIPT FOR PRINTER

1. *Checking typewritten copy.* When the manuscript has been typed, the author should read the typewritten copy for errors. All tables, figures, names, quotations, and citations in the typewritten copy must be verified by comparison with the original manuscript. The typewritten manuscript must be clear and legible, as well as correct. Be sure that symbols, signs, superscript letters and figures, etc., are unmistakable. For example, the symbol "Cl" (for chlorine) must be marked to show that it is not "C1," since the typewriter uses the same symbol for both the letter "l" and the figure "1"; the multiplication sign "×" must be marked plainly, to distinguish it from the letter "X." Assume that errors are present; if so, find and correct them. Typists are not infallible. The responsibility for uncorrected errors in figures, names, citations, and quotations rests entirely with the author, since the publisher has no means of discovering such errors. It is fatal to leave them for your critics to discover, after your paper has been published. A convenient method of checking tables is to have another person slowly read to you the figures, etc., from the original copy, while you follow the typewritten copy.

CORRECTIONS

2. *Corrections in body of manuscript.* If possible, write corrections in the body of the manuscript, not in the margin. If corrections are written in the margin, it

will be difficult to make necessary transpositions, by cutting and pasting. Do not destroy legibility by writing many words between the lines. When it is necessary to reconstruct a long sentence or a paragraph, typewrite the revision upon a separate slip of page width and paste this directly over the matter rewritten.

3. *Corrections horizontal.* Write corrections horizontally on the page.

4. *Corrections above line.* Place the corrections in the space above the line to which they apply so that the printer will see them before he reaches the words concerned.

5. *Erasure.* To cancel a word, draw a horizontal line through it. To cancel a single letter, draw a vertical line through it.

6. *Restoration.* To restore a word that has been canceled by mistake, rewrite the word above the one you have canceled, or make a series of dots under the word and write "Stet" in the margin.

7. *Substitution.* To replace one word by another, cancel the first word by drawing a horizontal line through it, and write the new word immediately above. *Never* write the new word directly upon the first.

8. *Indicating a paragraph.* When a word should begin a new paragraph, place the sign ¶ immediately before the word.

9. *Canceling a paragraph.* To cancel a paragraph division, write "No ¶" in the margin, and draw a "run-in" line from the indented word to the last word of the preceding sentence.

10. *Period.* A period may be indicated clearly by inclosing it in a small circle.

11. *Space between words.* To separate two words that have been written without space between them, draw a vertical line between them. (For example: Root|hair.)

12. *Canceling space between words.* To indicate that two words are to be brought together, connect them by means of half-circles above and below them. (For example: Foot‿note.)

13. *Reduction of capital letter.* To indicate that a capital letter should be printed as a small (lower-case) letter, draw through it an oblique line sloping downward from right to left.

14. *Italic capitals.* Four lines under a letter indicate that it is to be printed as an *ITALIC CAPITAL LETTER*.

15. *Capitals.* Three lines under a letter indicate that it is to be printed as a ROMAN CAPITAL LETTER.

16. *Small capitals.* Two lines under a letter indicate that it is to be printed as a SMALL CAPITAL LETTER.

17. *Italics.* One straight line under a letter or word indicates that it is to be printed in *italic type*.

18. *Bold-face.* One wavy line under a letter or word indicates that it is to be printed in **bold-face type.**

INSERTIONS

19. *Brief insertions.* To insert one word or a few words, write them above the line and indicate the place for their insertion by a caret (∧) placed below the line.

20. *Permissible method of insertion.* To insert a passage of several lines in a page of an initial draft of the manuscript, the following method may be used: Suppose the insertion is to be made in page 12 of the manuscript. The passage to be inserted should be written on a fresh slip of paper of page width. Mark this "A, Insert in page 12" and draw a circle around the passage. In the margin of page 12 write "Insert A," draw a circle around it, and from the circle draw a line to a caret ($_\wedge$) at the place where the insertion is to be made. Paste this slip securely to page 12. If several inserts are made in page 12, mark these "Insert A," "Insert B," "Insert C," "Insert D^x," indicating the last insert by the mark ^{x}.

21. *General method of insertion.* To insert a passage of several lines in a page of a later draft of the manuscript, the following method may be used: Suppose the insertion is to be made in page 7 of the manuscript. The passage to be inserted should be written on a fresh sheet of paper (full size). In the upper margin write "A, Insert in page 7," and draw a circle around the passage. Number this sheet "7A" and place it after page 7. In the margin of page 7 write "Insert A," draw a circle around it, and from the circle draw a line to a caret ($_\wedge$) at the place where the insertion is to be made. If several inserts are made in page 7, mark these "Insert A," "Insert B," "Insert C," "Insert D^x" (indicating the last insert by the mark ^{x}), and number the additional sheets "7A," "7B," "7C," "7D^x," placing them after page 7.

TRANSPOSITIONS

22. *Transposition by cancellation and insertion.* To transpose words, cancel them, and insert them in the proper place by one of the methods just given.

RENUMBERING PAGES

23. *Consecutive page numbers.* The methods given above refer to insertions and transpositions made in the preliminary drafts of an article. *Before the manuscript is submitted to an editor, or sent to a printer, all of the pages must be full-sized sheets numbered consecutively.*

Insertions and transpositions may be made by cutting and pasting. Smaller sheets included with the manuscript are likely to become separated, and lost. The pages may be renumbered by canceling the original numbers and writing the new numbers near the canceled ones. It is not necessary to have each manuscript page filled with typewriting; the printer will not leave a space if a lower part of a manuscript page contains no writing.

FINAL REVISIONS

24. *Finished manuscript.* The author is expected to make all final revisions in the typewritten manuscript. Only genuine errors may be corrected in the proofs. Alterations in the proofs are expensive and likely to introduce new errors and inconsistencies.

25. *Corrections in manuscript.* Remember that a manuscript in which there are no alterations usually indicates a careless author. If the changes are not too many and are made correctly and clearly, it will not be necessary to rewrite the pages.

26. *Order of material.* Before sending your manuscript to a publisher, be sure to have all parts in the proper order, as outlined below:

(a) Author's name and address to which proofs are to be sent.

(b) Title, name of author, footnote to title.

(c) Text material (each table and each long quotation being on a separate page).

(d) Bibliography (on a separate page).

(e) Footnotes (on a separate page).

(f) Legends for illustrations (on a separate page).

(g) Condensed title of 35 letters or less (on a separate page).

(h) Copy for illustrations.

KINDS OF TYPE AND THEIR INDICATION IN THE MANUSCRIPT

1. *Roman.* The type in general use is called Roman. There are three kinds of Roman type: (*a*) CAPITALS (caps), which may be indicated in the manuscript by drawing three lines under the word or letter to be capitalized; (*b*) SMALL CAPS (capital letters about half as high as caps), which may be indicated in the manuscript by drawing two lines under the letter or word; (*c*) lower-case letters (ordinary small letters). A diagonal line may be drawn through a capital letter to indicate that it should be printed as a small letter.

2. *Italics.* *In italic type, or italics, the letters slope up toward the right.* To indicate italic type, draw a single straight line under the letter, word, or figure. If italic capitals are desired, underscore with four straight lines.

3. *Bold-face.* Type with a conspicuous or heavy face is called **bold-face** or **black-face**. To indicate bold-face type, underscore with a wavy line. This type rarely should be used.

4. *Face and body of type.* A single piece of type cast by a monotype machine is a rectangular block of metal with a flat top which bears, in relief, a letter or other character. The upper or printing surface of the raised character is the face, and the block bearing the character is the body. The part of the flat top which projects beyond the base of the raised character is known as the shoulder.

5. *Size of type.* The sizes of type are classified according to the dimensions of the bodies. When the top of the type is viewed, the height of the body indicates the size of the type, the raised character always being slightly smaller than the top of the body. The following ex-

amples illustrate the common sizes, as they appear when printed:

This line is set in 6-point type.

This line is set in 8-point type.

This line is set in 9-point type.

This line is set in 10-point type.

This line is set in 11-point type.

This line is set in 12-point type.

The unit employed in sizes of type is the point, or $\frac{1}{72}$ inch. Thus 10-point type has a body 10 points ($\frac{10}{72}$ inch) high, and has a face, or raised character, slightly less in height, so that there will be a very small space between the printed lines. When 10-point type is used in composition without additional spaces between the lines, it is said to be set "solid." Usually, however, the lines are separated by additional spaces, or the type is "leaded." This may be done by thin strips of metal called "leads." But in the composition of books and periodicals the extra space generally is provided by casting the type on a larger body. In most work 10-point type is cast on a 12-point body, the effect being the same as if a 2-point lead were inserted between the lines. The type is then said to be 10-point leaded, or, more accurately, 10-point type on 12-point body. Scientific journals often employ 11-point type on 13-point body, with quotations set in 10-point on 12-point body; all other subsidiary matter (footnotes, bibliographies, tables, etc.) usually is set in 8-point type on 10-point body. This book is printed in 10-point on 12-point, with footnotes, etc., in 8-point on 10-point.

6. *Size of type page.* The unit employed in measuring the width and depth of the type page is termed a

12-point em (this term is literal, being the exact width of the capital letter "M"), or a pica, which is 12 points ($1\frac{3}{12}$ or $\frac{1}{6}$ inch long). Thus a type page that is $3\frac{1}{3}$ inches wide is twenty 12-point ems in width ($3\frac{1}{3} \div 1\frac{3}{12} = 20$).

7. *Spacing.* The em is used as a unit for measuring printed matter. An em of 12-point type (12 set) is 12 points ($\frac{1}{6}$ inch) wide (and also 12 points high); an em of 10-point (10 set) is 10 points wide; an em of 8-point (8 set) is 8 points wide. The em and halves of the em are used for indentation and spacing, and also for expressing the lengths of dashes. An em quad is a block of type that is one em in width; the ordinary dash (—), or em dash, is the width of an em quad. An en quad is half of the width of an em, and an en dash (–), used to separate page numbers in citations, is an en in width.

8. *Specifications.* Complete specifications for a publication include the styles and sizes of type for body, subsidiary matter, tables, references, headings, etc., the dimensions of the type page (in picas), the margins, the paper, the binding, instructions regarding illustrations, etc. The publisher ordinarily takes care of these details, but an editor or an author who is preparing copy ready for the printer should give considerable attention to all of these questions.

CAPITALS

The subject of capitalization is difficult to handle with definite rules, but capitals should be used according to a uniform style throughout a single article. For this reason a special revision of the manuscript should be made with the aim of making capitalization uniform.

1. *Proper nouns.* Capitalize a proper noun, designating an individual person or thing. Also, capitalize a

derivative of a proper noun if the derivative retains close association with the proper noun.

2. *First words*. Begin with a capital a sentence, a complete sentence directly quoted, a legend of a table or illustration, a center subheading, a paragraph side heading, or a topic in a table of contents.

3. *Titles of publications in text*. In the text, capitalize all important words in titles of books and periodicals; also capitalize important words in titles of chapters in books and of articles in periodicals.[6] (For example: Washburn's *An Introduction to the Principles of Physical Chemistry* contains a thorough discussion of osmotic pressure. Chapter I of Palladin's *Plant Physiology* is entitled "Assimilation of Carbon and of the Radiant Energy of the Sun by Green Plants." Accurate data are given by Adams in an article on "The Measurement of the Freezing-point Depression of Dilute Solutions," which appears in *The Journal of the American Chemical Society*.) In footnote citations and in bibliographies, capitalize the first word only in English titles of books and of articles in periodicals (p. 62).

4. *Scientific names*. In botanical and zoölogical work, capitalize the scientific names of genera, families, orders, classes, subdivisions, and divisions of plants and animals. (For example: *Triticum*, Gramineae, Glumiflorae, Monocotyledoneae, Angiospermae, Spermatophyta.)

5. *Common names derived from scientific names*. Do not capitalize common names derived from scientific names of plants and animals. (For example: ameba (amœba), angiosperm, bacillus.)

---

[6] The Government Printing Office capitalizes the first word and proper nouns only of titles of articles in books, magazines, and newspapers when referred to in the text.

6. *Table, figure, plate.* Do not capitalize *table, figure,* and *plate.*[7] (For example: The results given in table 2 have been plotted as graphs in figure 3. See curves I, IV, and VI.)

7. *Miscellaneous terms.* As a rule, do not capitalize such words as *plot, plat, series, class, exhibit, form, group, schedule, section, appendix, station,* etc., even when immediately followed by a figure or a capital letter.[8]

8. *Chemicals not capitalized.* Do not capitalize the names of chemical elements or compounds.

9. *Consistency.* Be consistent in the use of words regarding which usage differs. The words *volt, ampere, farad, ohm, coulomb,* and *watt* should not be capitalized. It is better to capitalize *India ink, Paris green, Prussian blue, plaster of Paris, Bordeaux mixture.* (Follow consistently a single unabridged dictionary, preferably *Webster's New International Dictionary.*)

10. *Manufactured products.* Capitalize the significant parts of the name of a manufactured product. (For example: Eversharp pencil, Cico paste, Royal typewriter, Ivory soap.)

[7] The Government Printing Office capitalizes any term (except page or pages) immediately preceding a Roman numeral. (For example: Article I, Chapter II, Figure IV, Group VI, Plate VIII.)

[8] The Government Printing Office capitalizes *appendix, exhibit, figure, form, group, plate, schedule,* and *table* when immediately followed by a figure or a capital letter. (For example: Appendix 1, Appendix A, Exhibit 2, Figure 8 (referring to illustrations), Form G, Group 6, Plate 9, Schedule K, Table 4, ect.) But it does not capitalize: abstract B, section A (of a land plat, etc.), station B (in surveying or like work), class 1, class A, volume 1, chapter 1, etc.

ITALICS

Indicate italic type in the manuscript by drawing a single straight line under the letters, words, or numerals that are to be italicized.

1. *Diagrams, drawings, and graphs.* Italicize letters used in diagrams, drawings, and graphs to represent points, lines, objects, etc., and use italics when reference to such letters is made in the text.[9] (Example of legend of diagram: "Fig. 1. Diagrammatic cross section of coconut pinna, lines *AB* and *AC* representing the two pinna wings, hinged to the midrib at *A*." Example of reference in the text: "If the diagram of figure 1 represents a cross section of a coconut pinna, then lines *AB* and *AC* represent the two wings, hinged to the pinna midrib at *A*.")

2. *Algebraic symbols.* Algebraic symbols and equations should be italicized. (For example: The general equation of a straight line may be written $Ax + By + C = 0$.) In equations, only the full-sized letters should be italicized; superscript and subscript letters should not be italicized. Numerals should not be italicized. (For example: $T^a + D_t - H^b = 2L_c$.)

3. *Genera and species.* In botanical, bacteriological, zoölogical, and geological work, italicize scientific names of genera, species, and varieties, and of genera alone.[10] (For example: *Phaseolus lunatus; Musa sapientum* Linn. var. *cinerea* (Blanco) Teod.; *Bacillus coli* (Escherich)

[9] The Government Printing Office uses italic for lower-case references and Roman for caps. (For example: The bolt a; a pinion, B; angle ab; line CD; points a, b, c.)

[10] Many zoölogical publications do not italicize scientific names. (For example: Mus musculus.) The Government Printing Office does not italicize the names of genera standing alone. (For example: Phytophthora, Zea, Triticum.)

Mig.; *Phytophthora*.)   But do not italicize names of classes, orders, and families.   When used in tables and in titles of articles, scientific names should not be italicized.

4. *Common names derived from scientific names.*   Do not italicize common names derived from scientific names of plants and animals.   (For example: Ameba (amœba), angiosperm, bacillus, bacterium, paramecium, protozoan, streptococci.)

5. *Books.*   As a rule, italicize titles of books, pamphlets, and periodicals when these appear in the text.   (For example: An excellent discussion is given in Russell's *Soil Conditions and Plant Growth*.)[11]   But do not italicize such titles when they appear in footnotes or in lists of citations.

6. *Subdivisions of books.*   Do not italicize titles of chapters in books or titles of articles in periodicals; use quotation marks.   (For example: Chapter V of Ganong's *The Living Plant* deals with "The Various Substances Made by Plants."   An article entitled "The Properties of Salt Solutions" appears in *The Journal of the American Chemical Society* for April, 1912.)[12]   In footnotes and in lists of citations, use neither italics nor quotation marks.

7. *Article.*   The word *the* or *a* should be italicized and capitalized when it begins the title of a book or a periodical.[13]   (For example: Copeland's *The Coconut* is used as

[11] The Government Printing Office uses quotation marks instead of italics for the title of a book.   (For example: A book entitled "The House of the Seven Gables.")

[12] The Government Printing Office capitalizes the first word and proper nouns only of titles of articles in books, magazines, and newspapers when referred to in the text.   (For example: "A story of life in New Orleans during the Mexican War.")

[13] This rule often is ignored in referring to the name of a periodical.

a textbook. The College of Agriculture publishes *The Philippine Agriculturist.*)

8. *Technical terms.* It is permissible to italicize a letter or word to which special attention is called. An unusual technical term, requiring formal definition, may be italicized the first time it appears in an article. When an expression is regarded as quoted, it should be inclosed in quotation marks. (For example: The term *atmometric index* will be used in place of the expression "evaporating power of the air.") It is best to avoid over-use of italics, capitals, and other special devices for emphasizing ideas. They often lead to an exaggeration of an idea or fact. If used excessively, they do not even give emphasis or distinction.

9. *Chemical and medical terms.* Do not italicize the names of chemicals, medicines, diseases, and anatomical parts. (For example: Sodium chloride, atropine, diabetes mellitus, esophagus.)

10. *Foreign words.* Do not italicize foreign words.[14] (For example: Intra-vitam staining, ceteris paribus, in medias res, in situ, en masse.)

NUMBERS

1. *General.* Use figures for all *definite* weights, measurements, percentages, and degrees of temperature. (For example: 6 kgm., 2 inches, 105.6 cc., 250°C.) Spell out all *indefinite* and *approximate* periods of time and all other numerals which are used in a general manner. (For example: One hundred years ago, thirty years old, about two and one-half hours, ten instances, three times.) Judgment must be exercised in this matter; for

[14] Many journals italicize foreign words or phrases that have not come into common use in English.

instance, in experimental data where periods of time are definite and of frequent occurrence, figures should be used. The general rule, however, is to spell out numbers wherever possible.

2. *Metric system.* The metric system of weights and measures should be employed in scientific publications, as a rule. Non-metric equivalents may be given in parentheses. (Where it is necessary or desirable to use a non-metric system, as in engineering, equivalent values expressed in metric units should be given in parentheses.)

3. *Abbreviations.* Universally understood abbreviations of metric weights and metric measures may be used in tables, footnotes, and citations, and in the text if used directly following figures. (For lists of abbreviations, see p. 44.) Non-metric units always should be spelled out, except in engineering.

4. *Temperatures.* Temperatures usually should be expressed in centigrade degrees. (For example: A temperature of 25.7°C. was used.) The equivalent in the Fahrenheit system may be given in parentheses if desired. (For example: 0°C. (32°F.).)

5. *Consistency.* Be consistent throughout the article in the use of figures; do not express small numbers in words in one paragraph and in figures in another.

6. *Time.* As a rule, employ figures for hours of the day, using a colon to separate hours and minutes. (For example: 7:00 a.m.; 3:30 p.m.)

7. *Dates.* Use figures for days of the month, spelling out the name of the month and omitting *d, th, st.* (For example: May 21, 1923; February 6, 1924.)

8. *Money.* Use figures for all sums of money written with a sign. (For example: $15.65; ₱25, *not* ₱25.00; however, definite precision sometimes requires the use of ciphers at right of decimal.)

9. *References to tables.* Use figures for all numbers taken from tabular matter.

10. *Beginning of sentence.* Never begin a sentence with a figure. Revise the sentence, or, if this is impossible, write the number in words.

11. *Twenty-one to ninety-nine.* Cardinal numbers from twenty-one to ninety-nine, inclusive, should be written with a hyphen. (For example: Twenty-nine, eighty-six.)

12. *Hyphens in ordinal numbers.* The words in ordinal numbers should be joined by hyphens. (For example: Thirty-fourth, one-hundred-and-eleventh.)

13. *Comma in figures.* In tabular matter, use a comma to separate a number of four or more figures, grouping three units to the right in all cases. In the text, omit a comma in a number containing four figures.

14. *Per cent.* Omission of a period after *per cent* is favored by most writers. (For example: The ash of plants constitutes only about 5 per cent of the dry weight, or about 2 per cent of the green weight. A 10 per cent increase.) Do not use the symbol %.

15. *Per cent and percentage.* Do not use *per cent* for *percentage.* *Per cent* should be preceded by a number. (For example: The results of three analyses gave the following percentages of sugar: 93.2, 93.1, and 92.9. There was an increase of 15 per cent in production.)

16. *Basis for percentage.* Always make clear the basis used for expressing percentages. (For example: The phrase "a 5 per cent solution of alcohol in water" does not tell whether the solution contains 5 grams of alcohol in 100 grams of solution, whether 100 cc. of the solution contain 5 cc. of alcohol, or whether some other basis has been used.)

17. *Fractions.* Decimal fractions usually should be employed in the metric system. Common fractions

used in an indefinite manner should be spelled out, joining the numerator to the denominator by a hyphen. (For example: One-half of the balance, two-thirds of the residue, about one-tenth of this quantity.) Use figures for common fractions when designating definite weights and measurements. (For example: $\frac{1}{4}$ grain, $\frac{1}{8}$ inch, $\frac{7}{12}$ gauge.) Very large fractions always should be expressed decimally.

18. *Half and quarter*. Compounds of *half* and *quarter* should be written with the hyphen. (For example: Half-liter; quarter-past. But: One half was dried; the other was not.)

19. *Plural*. Use of the plural form when referring to a quantity or measurement of more than one. (For example: About one and one-half kilometers; $1\frac{1}{4}$ inches.)

20. *Avoiding confusion*. Spell out numbers if confusion would be caused by the use of figures. (For example: Fifteen 200-watt Mazda lamps.)

ABBREVIATION OF UNITS OF WEIGHT AND MEASURE

The general rule regarding abbreviations is to employ only those abbreviations which you know are used by careful writers in your science, and to conform to the style of the publication in which your article is to appear. It is a good rule always to spell out the names of units of weights and measurements of all systems except the metric; the metric abbreviations are understood in all parts of the world, and so cause little confusion. This rule often is ignored, however, where brevity is essential.

A SET OF STANDARD ABBREVIATIONS

Standard abbreviations of units of weight and measure are given in the accompanying table.

The following general principles should be observed:

1. *Period.* A period should be used after each abbreviation.[15]

2. *Singular and plural.* The same form should be used for both singular and plural. (For example: 0.5 kgm., 12.3 kgm.)

3. *Small letters.* Small letters should be used for abbreviations.

Most common units of weight and measure and their abbreviations

UNIT	ABBREVIATION
are	a.
barrel	bbl.
board foot	bd. ft.
bushel	bu.
carat, metric	c.
centare	ca.
centigram	cgm.
centiliter	cl.
centimeter	cm.
chain	ch.
cubic centimeter (milliliter)	cc.
cubic centimeter	cu. cm.
cubic decimeter	cu. dm.
cubic dekameter	cu. dkm.
cubic foot	cu. ft.
cubic hectometer	cu. hm.
cubic inch	cu. in.
cubic kilometer	cu. km.
cubic meter	cu. m.
cubic mile	cu. mi.
cubic millimeter	cu. mm.
cubic yard	cu. yd.

[15] A number of authorities omit the period after the abbreviations of metric units, but this practice has not been adopted generally.

UNIT	ABBREVIATION
decigram	dgm.
deciliter	dl.
decimeter	dm.
decistere	ds.
dekagram	dkgm.
dekaliter	dkl.
dekameter	dkm.
dekastere	dks.
dram	dr.
dram, apothecaries'	dr. ap.
dram, avoirdupois	dr. av.
dram, fluid	fl. dr.
fathom	fath.
foot	ft.
firkin	fir.
furlong	fur.
gallon	gal.
hectare	ha.
hectogram	hgm.
hectoliter	hl.
hectometer	hm.
hogshead	hhd.
hundredweight	cwt.
inch	in.
kilogram	kgm.
kiloliter	kl.
kilometer	km.
link	li.
liquid	liq.
liter	l.
meter	m.
metric ton	t.
micron	μ
mile	mi.
milligram	mgm.
milliliter	ml.
millimeter	mm.

UNIT	ABBREVIATION
millimicron	mμ
minim	min.
ounce	oz.
ounce, apothecaries'	oz. ap.
ounce, avoirdupois	oz. av.
ounce, fluid	fl. oz.
ounce, troy	oz. t.
peck	pk.
pennyweight	dwt.
pint	pt.
pound	lb.
pound, apothecaries'	lb. ap.
pound, avoirdupois	lb. av.
pound, troy	lb. t.
quart	qt.
rod	rd.
scruple, apothecaries'	s. ap.
square centimeter	sq. cm.
square chain	sq. ch.
square decimeter	sq. dm.
square dekameter	sq. dkm.
square foot	sq. ft.
square hectometer	sq. hm.
square inch	sq. in.
square kilometer	sq. km.
square meter	sq. m.
square mile	sq. mi.
square millimeter	sq. mm.
square rod	sq. rd.
square yard	sq. yd.
stere	s.
troy	t.
yard	yd.

It will be noted that no abbreviations are given for
"gram" and "grain." These two words always should
be spelled out, because errors are likely to result from

the use of such abbreviations as "g.," "gr.," and "grs." In medical work, especially, misinterpretation of such an abbreviation can lead to serious harm.

ABBREVIATIONS OF THE AMERICAN INSTITUTE OF ELECTRICAL ENGINEERS

The following list shows the abbreviations employed by The American Institute of Electrical Engineers.[16] Many engineering publications use this set of abbreviations.

TERM	ABBREVIATION
alternating current	spell out, or a-c. when used as compound adjective
amperes	spell out
boiler horse power	boiler h.p.
brake horse power	b.h.p.
British thermal units	B.t.u.
candle power	c.p.
centigrade	cent.
centimeters	cm.
circular mils	cir. mils
counter electromotive force	counter e.m.f.
cubic	cu.
diameter	spell out
direct current	spell out, or d-c. when used as compound adjective
electric horse power	e.h.p.
electromotive force	e.m.f.

[16] Anonymous: Suggestions to authors. 1919. 11 p. New York: American Institute of Electrical Engineers.

TERM	ABBREVIATION
Fahrenheit	Fahr.
feet	ft.
foot-pounds	ft-lb.
gallons	gal.
grains	gr.
gram-calories	g-cal.
grams	g.
high-pressure cylinder	spell out
hours	hr.
inches	in.
indicated horse power	i.h.p.
kilogram-calories	kg-cal.
kilogram-meters	kg-m.
kilograms	kg.
kilometers	km.
kilovolts	kv.
kilovolt-amperes	kv-a.
kilowatt-hours	kw-hr.
kilowatts	kw.
magnetomotive force	m.m.f.
mean effective pressure	spell out
meter-kilograms	m-kg.
meters	m.
microfarad	spell out
miles	mi.
miles per hour per second	mi. per hr. per sec.
milligrams	mg.
millimeters	mm.
minutes	min.
ohms	spell out
per	spell out
percentage	per cent (or % in tabular matter)
pounds	lb.
power-factor	spell out

TERM	ABBREVIATION
revolutions per minute......................	rev. per min. (or r.p.m. in tabular matter)
seconds....................................	sec.
square.....................................	sq.
square-root-of-mean-square.................	r.m.s.
ton-mile...................................	spell out
tons.......................................	spell out
volt-amperes...............................	spell out
volts......................................	spell out
watt-hours.................................	watt-hr.
watts......................................	spell out
watts per candle power.....................	watts per c.p.
yards......................................	yd.

NAMES OF PLANTS AND ANIMALS

PLANTS

1. *Complete name.* A complete plant name should include the name of the genus (in italics), the name of the species (in italics), and the abbreviated designation of the person who named the plant (in Roman type). (For example: *Oryza sativa* Linn.)[17] It often is desirable to add the common name of the plant and the name of the family (both in Roman type). (For example: *Shorea polysperma* Merr. (tanguile), Dipterocarpaceae; *Hemileia vastatrix* Berk. and Br. (coffee rust), Pucciniaceae.) Unfortunately, very many plants have each received several common and scientific names. Where names differ in standard or commonly used works, one is chosen and the others are regarded as synonyms. If a

[17] A comma often is used between the species name and the authority for the name. (For example: *Oryza sativa,* Linn.)

synonym is much used, it is customary to insert it (in parentheses) after the accepted name. In an index, accepted names usually are printed in Roman type, and synonyms in italics. In tables and in titles, names of genera and species should be printed in Roman type.

2. *Omission of family name.* Often the family name may be omitted, especially if the plant is well known.

3. *Necessity of scientific name.* The scientific name, in addition to the common name, should be given when the plant is first mentioned in an article. Aim constantly to use names that will be understood by foreign readers, many of whom must translate an article before they can understand it. For example, *Manihot utilissima* is universally understood; but the common name camoteng cahoy would be unintelligible to readers in many parts of the world. The scientific name may be inclosed in parentheses after the common name. (For example: The experiments described in this paper deal with the growth of rice (*Oryza sativa* Linn.).)

4. *Use of common name.* In papers dealing with agriculture, the scientific name of a well-known plant need not be repeated; after the scientific name has been given once, the plant may be referred to in the rest of the article by its common name.

5. *Capitalization.* The generic name should be capitalized, and the specific name usually should not be capitalized.[18] There is good authority, however, for capitalizing names of species derived from generic names, or from names of persons. (For example: *Acer Negundo, Ustilago Zeae, Magnolia Soulangeana.*)

6. *Variety name.* Capitalize the vernacular names of plant varieties (Yellow Dent corn, Binocol rice, Carabao

[18] The Government Printing Office never capitalizes the specific name. (For example: *Ustilago zeae.*)

mango, New Era cowpeas), but not the latinized names of varieties (*Lathyrus palustris* Linn. var. *linearifolius* Ser.).

ANIMALS

7. *Complete name.* In articles on zoölogy or one of its branches, such as entomology, names of animals should be given in a form similar to that used for plant names. (For example: *Agromyza destructor* Malloch (bean fly), Family Agromyzidae, Order Diptera; *Bubalus bubalis* Lyd. (carabao), Bovidae; *Equus caballus* Linn. (horse), Equidae.)

8. *Use of common name.* In articles on agriculture well-known kinds of animals may be referred to by their common names; the complete scientific name may be given only at the beginning of the article, or it may be omitted entirely. (For example: Berkshire swine, carabao, cattle, horse, Barred Plymouth Rock fowls.)

TABLES

1. *Importance.* The first step in the analysis of experimental data is to arrange them in the form of tables. This part of the work requires a great deal of study before the best scheme for bringing out relations is found. Two general types of tables usually should be prepared: (a) those which contain the original data, including actual observations and measurements, and (b) those which contain derived data, bringing out special points and conclusions. A large part of the work of interpretation of the data will have been completed when well-arranged tables have been made.

2. *Unity.* Each table should be a unit. A table is a short-cut means of presenting facts to the reader, and a table (like a sentence, paragraph, or composition)

should present one subject with distinctness. Do not attempt to bring out in a single table several comparisons of very different kinds. Avoid large tables; they are confusing.

3. *Clearness.* The form of the table should be arranged to secure greatest clearness. For each kind of comparison of data, there usually is one form of table which brings out the comparison most clearly and systematically. In addition to the absolute figures repre-

TABLE 1

Relation of spacing to character and yield of rice (variety number 663) grown from June 15 to November 15, 1915

SPACING	NUMBER OF CULMS PER PLANT	HEIGHT OF PLANTS*	YIELD OF ROUGH RICE PER SQUARE METER
		cm.	kgm.
10 by 10 cm..............	3.0	126	0.44
10 by 15 cm..............	3.6	128	0.39
15 by 20 cm..............	4.7	129	0.28‡
20 by 20 cm..............	5.2	†	0.20
25 by 25 cm..............	6.3	127	0.19

* Height data were obtained at the time of flowering.

† Data were lost.

‡ Approximate only.

senting original observations, the table, as a rule, should include percentages, ratios, totals, averages, etc.; the latter are of great value in making comparisons.

4. *Accuracy.* The accuracy of the data in each table should be checked. Each item in the table must be checked for correctness.

5. *Size.* If possible, the table should be compiled so as to fit the page of the publication. When large tables are required, the method of handling them should be left to the judgment of the printer. A folder should not be insisted upon unless it is absolutely unavoidable.

Folders are not only very costly, but are unwieldy for the reader to handle. If a table is too large to come within the width of the page, it may be possible to set it lengthwise on the page. If it will fit neither crosswise

TABLE 2

Principal export crops of the Philippine Islands

CROP	AREA OF CULTIVATED LAND	ARTICLE OF EXPORT	VALUE OF EXPORT FOR YEAR 1918
	hectares		*pesos*
Abaca................	518,000	Manila hemp	116,383,100
Coconuts	340,000 {	Coconut oil	63,328,318
		Copra	10,377,030
Tobacco..............	79,000	Tobacco*	12,685,248
Sugar cane...........	208,000	Sugar	31,608,780
Maguey..............	32,800	Maguey	3,736,108

* Manufactured and unmanufactured tobacco.

TABLE 3

Values of the conductance ratio* at different concentrations for three types of salts at 18°C.

TYPE	EXAMPLE	CONDUCTANCE RATIOS		
		0.001 normal	0.010 normal	0.050 normal
Uni-univalent...........	KNO_3	0.96	0.92	0.87
Uni-bivalent........... {	$BaCl_2$ K_2SO_4 }	0.94	0.87	0.78
Bi-bivalent.............	$MgSO_4$	0.86	0.64	0.47

* The conductance ratio represents approximately the degree of ionization of a salt.

nor lengthwise, then it may be possible to keep it within bounds by setting it in 6-point type, the smallest size used for book and periodical work. If this method fails, the table may be spread across two facing pages,

as shown in table 7. Should all of these methods prove
unavailing, the only recourse is to print the table on a
folder.

6. *Large tables in manuscript.* If a table requires a
larger sheet than that used for the text of the manuscript,
the sheet may be folded and inserted in place as one of
the manuscript pages.

7. *Each table on separate page.* Each individual table
should be typewritten on a separate sheet of paper,

TABLE 4

*Diurnal fluctuations in apparent leaf width for banana plants,
each value representing the average for forty-six leaves,
on May 17, 1919*

TIME OF OBSERVATION	LEAVES IN SUN		LEAVES IN PARTIAL SHADE	
	Actual	Relative	Actual	Relative
	cm.		*cm.*	
8:00 a.m........	21.7	100	25.0	100
10:00 a.m........	16.7	77	23.7	95
12:00 noon.......	7.4	34	19.4	78
2:00 p.m........	17.3	80	23.1	92
4:00 p.m........	20.1	93	24.4	98
6:00 p.m........	22.2	102	25.1	100

without any of the text on the same page. This is
necessary to facilitate typesetting. When the place for
a table is reached in typewriting a manuscript, the text
sheet should be removed from the typewriter (no matter
where the typewriting ends), and a new sheet should be
put in the typewriter; only the table (preceded by its
heading and followed by its footnotes) should be written
on this sheet. The text should be continued on a fresh
sheet of paper. If, through oversight or otherwise, it
becomes necessary to insert a table in a full page, it
should be treated as an insert (p. 31).

8. *Open and ruled tables.* Tables may be either open or ruled; the former generally are used in tables of only two columns, though they are employed exclusively in some periodicals (for example, in *The Journal of the American Chemical Society*). The suggestions given below refer to ruled tables.

9. *Examples.* Sample tables are given on pages 52–59. Care should be taken to prepare each table in exactly the proper form.

TABLE 5

Salt proportions of nutrient solutions, having an osmotic value of 1.0 atmosphere, and corresponding yields of wheat

SOLUTION NUMBER	VOLUME-MOLECULAR PROPORTIONS			MEAN DRY WEIGHT OF TOPS	
	KH_2PO_4	$Ca(NO_3)_2$	$MgSO_4$	Actual	Relative
				mgm.	
1	5.0	5.0	90.0	98.9 ± 1.3	67
2	5.0	47.5	47.5	140.0 ± 1.5	95
3	5.0	90.0	5.0	103.8 ± 1.5	70
4	33.3	33.3	33.3	136.7 ± 1.8	92
5	47.5	5.0	47.5	120.7 ± 1.6	81
6	47.5	47.5	5.0	107.5 ± 1.5	73
7	90.0	5.0	5.0	125.9 ± 1.7	85
8	50.0	18.0	32.0	148.1 ± 1.7	100

10. *Heading, or title.* Note the way in which the heading is made. The tables are numbered consecutively throughout each article. The word "Table," followed by an Arabic number, appears as a center heading (printed in 6-point caps). The legend, or description, of the table is centered above the body of the table; only the first word and proper names have capital initials; the legend is printed in 8-point italics. Each word of the legend is underscored with a single straight line to indicate italic type to the printer. The legend should be

TABLE 6

*Statistical data of the calcium and magnesium content of the ash of the humerus and femur of various groups of female rats**

| | HUMERUS | | | | FEMUR | | | |
| | Calcium | | Magnesium | | Calcium | | Magnesium | |
	mgm.	per cent	mgm.	per cent	mgm.	per cent	mgm.	per cent
Reference controls, 100 days old:								
Mean..................	27.57	37.83	0.605	0.84	57.99	37.66	1.291	0.84
Standard deviation....	4.20	0.31	0.051	0.06	9.37	0.37	0.178	0.05
Probable error of mean.	0.90	0.07	0.011	0.01	2.00	0.08	0.038	0.01
Coefficient of variability.	15.25	0.83	8.43	6.60	16.16	0.98	13.82	5.62
Controls, 150 days old:								
Mean..................	36.36	37.80	0.826	0.85	75.85	37.76	1.703	0.85
Standard deviation....	5.84	0.60	0.245	0.16	15.92	0.48	0.429	0.10
Probable error of mean.	1.19	0.12	0.050	0.03	3.24	0.10	0.087	0.02
Coefficient of variability.	16.06	1.59	29.69	18.94	20.99	1.26	25.20	12.25
Thyroparathyroidectomized rats, 150 days old:								
Mean..................	25.56	37.28	0.634	0.92	56.55	37.22	1.358	0.89
Standard deviation....	3.76	0.55	0.137	0.14	11.28	0.40	0.330	0.10
Probable error of mean.	0.73	0.11	0.027	0.03	2.11	0.07	0.062	0.02
Coefficient of variability.	14.69	1.48	21.62	14.86	19.95	1.07	24.28	10.89

* From data given by F. S. Hammett.

self-explanatory and should enable the reader to understand the table without referring to the text of the article. It should be broad enough to include all the data in the table; make it definite—allow only one meaning.

11. *Box heads.* The box heads, which are the heads at the top of columns in a table, appear in small caps (6-point). The secondary heads, when present, are printed in ordinary type (6-point lower-case).

12. *Units of measurement.* In the stub (first column) units of quantity are placed on the right, as shown in table 1. In other columns such units are given below the line under the box heads, and printed in 6-point italics. For example, in the third column "*cm.*" (underscored in the manuscript to indicate italics) appears below the line under the box head "Height of plants." In the fourth column "*kgm.*" appears below the line under the box head.

13. *Body of table.* Columns consisting of words in the body of the table should appear in ordinary type. Figure columns should be aligned on the right; reading columns, on the left. Figure columns should be separated from perpendicular rules at least an en space (p. 35); decimals should be aligned; figures should be centered in the columns. Omissions should be indicated by blank spaces; the reasons for such omissions should be explained clearly, in footnotes. If possible, the body of the table is printed in 8-point type; it sometimes is necessary to use 6-point type.

14. *Footnotes.* Observe that explanatory footnotes to tables are indicated by means of standard footnote reference marks (*, †, ‡, §, etc.) placed after the words or the numbers to which the footnotes refer.[19] The foot-

[19] Lower-case superscript letters are used instead of symbols by many journals. The letters usually are placed *after* the words or *before* the numbers to which the footnotes refer.

F. T., age twenty

TIME	URINE VOLUME	CYSTINE	CYSTINE N	AMINO-ACID N	CYSTINE N ÷ AMINO-ACID N	TOTAL N	AMINO ACID ÷ TOTA
day	cc.	mgm.	mgm.	mgm.	per cent	grams	per c
I	1,610	750	86.4	322	26.8	6.90	4.
II	460	546	63.6	280	22.7	5.66	4.9
III	910	484	56.4	234	24.1	5.54	4.2
IV	1,150	427	49.7	242	20.5	5.10	4.7
V	1,130	431	50.2	250	20.0	4.57	5.
VI	955	336	39.1	255	15.3	3.86	6.6
VII	1,160	269	31.3	246	12.7	3.52	7.
VIII	1,270	180	21.0	266	7.9	3.72	7.1
IX	1,280	118	13.2	240	5.7	3.36	7.1
X	1,145	183	21.3	260	8.2	3.54	7.3
XI	1,275	178	20.8	255	8.1	3.65	7.0
XII	1,375	165	19.2	245	7.8	3.22	7.6
XIII	1,500	270	31.5	225	14.0	3.51	6.4
XIV	1,575	394	45.9	188	24.4	3.76	5.6
XV	1,540	277	32.3	136	23.7	3.51	3.9
XVI	785	338	39.4	197	20.0	3.49	5.6
XVII	920	386	45.0	162	27.7	3.78	4.3

* The data given here are from the results of Looney, Berglund,

7

s, weight 180 pound*

H	ACIDITY (−) ALKALINITY (+)	AMMONIA N	REMARKS
	cc.	mgm.	
.1	−115	346	Sediment; large amounts of cystine crystals.
.3	−186	300	Sediment; large amounts of cystine crystals.
.5	− 93	218	Sediment; large amounts of cystine crystals.
.5	−118	242	
.5	−103	100	15 grams sodium bicarbonate. Sediment; cystine crystals still present.
.6			15 grams sodium bicarbonate. Sediment; single cystine crystals still present.
.6			15 grams sodium bicarbonate. Sediment; no crystals.
.5			15 grams sodium bicarbonate. Sediment; a few crystals.
.4			15 grams sodium bicarbonate. Sediment; a few cystine crystals present.
.8			20 grams sodium bicarbonate. Sediment; no cystine crystals.
.6			20 grams sodium bicarbonate.
.5			20 grams sodium bicarbonate.
.6			Bicarbonate discontinued. Sediment; no crystals.
.9			Sediment; no crystals.
.7			4 grams atophan. Sediment; no crystals.
.7			Atophan discontinued. Sediment; no crystals.
.7			Sediment; no crystals.

ves.

notes are typewritten on the sheet bearing the table. Each footnote is preceded by a symbol and is indented as a paragraph. Footnotes are printed in 8-point type, leaded (p. 34).

15. *Special type.* Bold-face and italic type may be used to distinguish different classes of data in a table. Uniform type treatment, however, is desirable. In general, it is well to avoid unnecessary multiplicity of sorts of type, because typesetting machines are now used almost universally.

16. *Cross rules.* Care should be taken that as few cross rules as possible are used. A cross rule is necessary at the top of the table, another is needed below the box heads, and a third is needed at the bottom of the table. Any additional cross rules increase the cost of printing. Where a line of demarcation is necessary, it can be indicated effectively and inexpensively by a blank space, which can be composed by the typesetting machine.

17. *Spacing.* In the printed table, the figure columns should be cast to cover the normal requirements of the figure entries or wording of box heads; spaces between perpendicular rules, if possible, should be the same; the balance of the space may be put in the stub (first column) or other reading columns. Tables should be set leaded (p. 34). In long tables, grouping the horizontal lines of figures in groups of four lines, by a double lead, makes the table easier to read and aids in preventing inaccurate reading.

18. *References.* References to tables should be made by number. (For example: By reference to table 10; the data presented in table 3.)

FOOTNOTES

1. *Reference numbers in text.* Footnotes pertaining to the text should be numbered consecutively (from 1 up)

throughout each article and indicated by superscript numerals ([1,2,3,4] etc.).[20] The reference numeral to the footnote should be placed in the text, after the punctuation mark that follows the word or sentence to which the footnote refers. Indicate the superscript numeral by typewriting it above the line and placing a V-shaped mark under the numeral. Observe that these references apply to the text only; tabulations employ a separate series of symbols for each table (see p. 57). If mathematical formulas containing exponents appear in the text, care should be taken to avoid confusing exponents and footnote reference numbers.

2. *Footnotes at end of manuscript.* Footnotes should not be written in the body of the text; the text should have the reference numbers only. Footnotes should be typewritten on one or more separate sheets (as many footnotes to a sheet as convenient). Each footnote should be indented as a paragraph, and should be preceded by a superscript numeral corresponding to the reference number in the body of the manuscript. The sheets bearing footnotes should be put at the end of the text copy, each sheet bearing the word "Footnotes," inclosed in a circle.

This method is necessary in order to facilitate composition on the typesetting machines. When printed, each footnote will be inserted at the foot of the proper page.

3. *Misuse of footnotes.* Use footnotes only where they are indispensable. Include important material in the text; omit irrelevant material.

[20] In a few journals the footnotes are numbered consecutively (from 1 up) on each printed page. In this case the footnotes should be numbered from 1 up on each page of the manuscript and indicated by superscript numerals. The numbering may be changed when the page proof is made up, so that the first footnote on each printed page will be "1," and the second "2," etc.

LITERATURE CITATIONS

Citations to literature may be given in footnotes, distributed through the article, or they may be placed in the form of a bibliography at the end of the article. The citations should be written according to the form used by the journal in which the paper is to be published. Each item in every citation must be verified by the author. Responsibility for the accuracy and completeness of citations must rest with the author. The editor can not be expected to verify your citations; he may aid you in revising the form to suit the style of the journal, but he can not be expected to look up spelling, figures, etc., nor supply data that you have omitted.

Since most journals give the citations at the end of the article in the form of a bibliography, the directions given below apply primarily to such lists. Four methods are included. Each of the four methods has wide usage. The third method, however, seems to the authors of this book to have some advantages not possessed by the others. If the list is short, the heading "Literature cited" may be employed; if the list is comprehensive, the heading "Bibliography" may be used.

FIRST METHOD

1. *Text reference to citation.* Reference to a citation should be made by means of the author's name followed by a reference number in parentheses. The references should be numbered consecutively in the order in which they are given in the text. For example, the text may appear as follows:

The methods used were essentially the same as those employed by Lehenbauer (1). Fawcett (2) has investigated the growth of fungi in relation to temperature. Physiological temperature indices have been derived by Livingston (3) for the study of plant growth in relation to climatic conditions.

2. *Arrangement in bibliography.* The bibliography should be put at the end of the article. It should begin on a new sheet of paper; this is necessary to facilitate revision and typesetting. The first sheet should bear the center heading "Literature cited" or "Bibliography," which will be printed in capitals of the type used for the bibliography.

The citations should be arranged in consecutive numerical order. Each citation should be preceded by the reference number; it should begin flush with the left-hand edge of the writing, and second and succeeding lines should be indented 10 spaces on the typewriter. For example:

(1) LEHENBAUER, P. A.: Growth of maize seedlings in relation to temperature. Physiol. Res., 1914, i, 247–288.
(2) FAWCETT, H. S.: The temperature relations of growth in certain parasitic fungi. Univ. California Pub. Agric. Sci., 1921, iv, 183–232.
(3) LIVINGSTON, B. E.: Physiological temperature indices for the study of plant growth in relation to climatic conditions. Physiol. Res., 1916, i, 399–420.

Journals with numbered volumes

3. *Items and form.* Each citation of an article in a journal should include the following items:

(*a*) *Name of author.* The surname is followed by a comma and initials (or given names), all in large and small caps. (Three lines placed below a letter indicate that this letter should be printed in caps; two lines indicate small caps.) The author's name is followed by a colon. (For example: TOWNSEND, M. R.:) If there are several authors, only the name of the first should be inverted. (For example: NOYES, A. A., AND K. G. FALK:)

(b) *Title of paper*, exactly like the original in wording and punctuation. Title ends with a period. Only proper names are capitalized, except when the title is in Danish, Dutch, or German.

(c) *Abbreviated name of serial publication* (journal, periodical, etc.), followed by a comma. Standard abbreviations should be used for the names of serial publications (p. 79).

(d) *Year of publication of the article*, followed by a comma. (For example: 1910,)

(e) *Volume number, given in Roman numerals* (made with small letters), followed by a comma. (For example: xxxii,)

(f) *Page numbers*. The number of the first page of the article should be separated by an en dash (indicated by an extra-length hyphen) from the number of the last page, and the latter should be followed by a period.

(g) *Number of plates and text figures*. The serial numbers of these are given in Arabic figures. (For example: Pl. 1–5, fig. 1–9. Fig. 1–11. 8 pl., 9 fig.)

(1) ADOLPH, EDWARD F., AND WILLIAM B. FULTON: The effects of exposure to high temperatures upon the circulation in man. Amer. Jour. Physiol., 1924, lxvii, 573–588. Fig. 1–3.

(2) CARREL, ALEXIS: Tissue culture and cell physiology. Physiol. Rev., 1924, iv, 1–20.

(3) CONN, H. J.: Future methods of soil bacteriological investigations. Centralbl. f. Bakteriol., Parasitenk. u. Infekt.-Krankh., 1910, 2, xxv, 454–457. [Note the series number "2."]

(4) GEILING, E. M. K., AND A. C. KOLLS: Pharmacological action of primary albumose in unanesthetized dogs. Jour. Pharmacol. and Exper. Therap., 1924, xxiii, 29–43. Fig. 1–5.

(5) MACLEOD, J. J. R.: Insulin. Physiol. Rev., 1924, iv, 21–68. Fig. 1–7.

(6) PARSONS, FLOYD W.: Pioneering beyond the rim. Saturday Evening Post, May 5, 1923, cvc[45], 22–23, 123–125, 129. [Note that the superscript figure ([45]) following the volume (cvc) shows that this article appears in number 45 of volume cvc. This method of citation is used when each issue, or number, of the periodical begins with page 1. Also note that the exact date of issue is given.]

(7) PAVLOV, P. N.: Molecular state of pure liquids. Jour. Russ. Phys. Chem. Soc., 1916, xlviii, 1175–1196. Cited in Chem. Absts., 1917, xi, 1583–1584. [A citation taken from an abstract journal or any publication other than the original must show the source.]

(8) SWIFT, HOMER F.: The pathogenesis of rheumatic fever. Jour. Exper. Med., 1924, xxxix, 497–508. Pl. 22–27.

Experiment station bulletins

4. *Items and form.* In citing experiment station bulletins and other issues of serial publications bearing an individual number but no volume number, the bulletin number should be used like the volume number of a journal. But the bulletin number should be given in Arabic numerals. (For example: Univ. Illinois Agric. Exper. Sta. Bull. 165, 463–579.)

(1) BROWN, WILLIAM H., AND ARTHUR F. FISCHER: Philippine bamboos. Philippine Bur. Forestry Bull. 15, 1–32. 1918. Pl. 1–33.

(2) KELLEY, W. P.: Ammonification and nitrification in Hawaiian soils. Hawaii Agric. Exper. Sta. Bull. 37, 1–52. 1915.

(3) MITCHELL, H. H., AND H. S. GRINDLEY: The element of uncertainty in the interpretation of feeding experiments. Univ. Illinois Agric. Exper. Sta. Bull. 165, 463–579. 1913. Fig. 1–8.

Books

5. *Items and form.* In the citation of a book, the name of the author and the title are given in the same

way as in the citation of a journal article.   The remainder
of the book citation departs somewhat from the form
described above.   An example will illustrate the form
used in citing a book:

(1) BAYLISS, WILLIAM MADDOCK: Principles of general physiol-
      ogy. 1920. 3rd ed., xxvi + 862 p., 261 fig. London:
      Longmans, Green, and Company.

Note that the date of publication (copyright date)
is given after the title of the book.   The edition (3rd ed.)
and the number of pages (xxvi + 862 p.) are given next,
the introductory pages (xxvi) being shown in Roman
numerals (made with small letters, not capitals).   The
number of pages is followed by a comma and the number
of figures (261 fig.).   Then the place of publication is
given, followed by a colon and the name of the publisher.

(1) BAILEY, FREDERICK RANDOLPH, AND ADAM MARION MILLER:
      Text-book of embryology. 1916. 3rd ed., xvi + 655 p.,
      515 fig. New York: William Wood and Company.
(2) FUNK, CASIMIR: The vitamines. Authorized translation
      from second German edition by Harry E. Dubin. 1922.
      502 p., 73 fig. Baltimore: Williams & Wilkins Company.
(3) JACKSON, C. M. (EDITOR): Morris's human anatomy, a com-
      plete systematic treatise by English and American
      authors. 1921. 6th ed., xiv + 1507 p., 1164 fig. Phila-
      delphia: P. Blakiston's Son & Company.
(4) McFARLAND, JOSEPH: A text-book upon the pathogenic bac-
      teria and protozoa for students of medicine and physi-
      cians. 1919. 9th ed., 858 p., 330 fig. Philadelphia and
      London: W. B. Saunders Company.

Yearbooks

6. *Items and form*. An example will illustrate the
form that should be used:

(1) BACK, E. A.: Danger of introducing fruit flies in the United
      States. 1918. U. S. Dept. Agric. Yearbook for 1917,
      185–196.

7. *Text reference to citation.* Reference to a citation should be made by means of the author's name followed by an abbreviated year number in parentheses. (For example: Jennings ('16).) If reference is made to several papers published in the same year by one author, use the suffixes a, b, c, etc., after the year symbol (the suffixes being chosen according to the order in which you mention the articles). (For example: Jennings ('16 a, '16 b).) Note that the suffix is separated from the symbol by a single space.

8. *Arrangement in bibliography.* The bibliography should be placed at the end of the article. It should begin on a new sheet of paper; this is necessary to facilitate revision and printing. The first sheet should bear the heading "Literature cited" or "Bibliography," which will be printed in capitals of the type used for the bibliography.

The citations should be arranged in alphabetical order, according to authors' names. A number of articles by the same author should be listed in chronological order, according to the year of publication. The author's name should be typewritten flush with the left-hand edge of the writing, and second and succeeding lines should be indented 10 spaces on the typewriter.

Journals with numbered volumes

9. *Items and form.* Each citation of an article in a journal should include the following items:

(a) *Name of author.* The surname is followed by a comma and initials (or given names), all in large and small caps. (Three lines placed below a letter indicate that this letter should be printed in caps; two lines indicate small caps.) (For example: HEGNER, R. W.) If there are several authors, names of all should be inverted. (For example: DODGE, R., AND BENEDICT, F. G.)

(b) *Year of publication of the article.* (For example: 1919) An extra space should precede this number, and an extra space (but no punctuation) should follow it.

(c) *Title of paper*, exactly like the original in wording and punctuation. Title should end with a period. Only proper names should be capitalized, except when the title is in Danish, Dutch, or German.

(d) *Abbreviated name of serial publication* (journal, periodical, etc.), followed by a comma. Standard abbreviations should be used (p. 79).

(e) *Volume number*, followed by a comma. (For example: vol. 53, T. 21, Bd. 68,)

(f) *Page numbers.* The number of the first page should be separated by an en dash (indicated by an extra-length hyphen) from the number of the last page, and the latter should be followed by a period. (For example: pp. 463–692. S. 110–111.)

IVANOW, J. 1913 Action de l'alcool sur les spermatozoides des mammifères. Compt. rend. Soc. Biol. Paris, T. 74, pp. 480–484.

JENNINGS, H. S. 1908 Heredity, variation and evolution in Protozoa. II. Heredity and variation of size and form in Paramecium, etc. Proc. Amer. Philosoph. Soc., vol. 47, pp. 393–546.
1916 Heredity, variation and the results of selection in the uniparental reproduction of Difflugia corona. Genetics, vol. 1, pp. 407–534.

OEHLER, R. 1913 Zur Gewinnung reiner Trypanosomenstämme. Centralbl. f. Bakteriol., Parasitenk. u. Infekt.-Krankh., Abt. I, Orig., Bd. 70, S. 110–111.

PAINTER, T. S. 1923 Studies in mammalian spermatogenesis. II. The spermatogenesis of man. Jour. Exper. Zoöl., vol. 37, pp. 291–334.

TAYLOR, C. V. 1920 a Demonstration of the neuromotor apparatus in Euplotes by the method of microdissection. Univ. California Pub. in Zoölogy, vol. 19, pp. 403–470. 1920 b An accurately controllable micropipette. Science, vol. 51, 617.

Experiment station bulletins

10. *Items and form*. In citing experiment station bulletins and other issues of serial publications bearing an individual number but no volume number, use the form shown by the following examples:

DODGE, R., AND BENEDICT, F. G. 1915 Psychological effects of alcohol. Carnegie Inst. Washington Pub. no. 232, pp. 1–281.

MITCHELL, H. H., AND GRINDLEY, H. S. 1913 The element of uncertainty in the interpretation of feeding experiments. Univ. Illinois Agric. Exper. Sta. Bull. no. 165, pp. 463–579.

PEARL, R., AND MINER, J. R. 1914 A table for estimating the probable significance of statistical constants. Maine Agric. Exper. Sta. Bull. no. 226.

Books

11. *Items and form*. In the citation of a book, the name of the author, the year of publication (copyright date), and the title are given in the same way as in the citation of a journal article. The following examples will illustrate the form used:

DAVENPORT, C. B. 1908 Experimental morphology. New York and London: The Macmillan Company. xviii + 509 pp.

HEGNER, R. W., AND TALIAFERRO, W. H. 1924 Human protozoology. New York and London: The Macmillan Company. 597 pp.

LAVERAN, A., AND MESNIL, F. 1912 Trypanosomes et Trypanosomiases. 2nd ed., Paris: Masson et cie. viii + 1000 pp.

LILLIE, R. S. 1924 Protoplasmic action and nervous action. Chicago: The University of Chicago Press. 417 pp.

Yearbooks

12. *Items and form*. An example will illustrate the form that should be used:

BACK, E. A. 1918 Danger of introducing fruit flies in the United States. U. S. Dept. Agric. Yearbook for 1917, pp. 185–196.

THIRD METHOD

13. *Text reference to citation*. Reference to a citation should be made by means of the author's name followed by the year of publication, the year number being inclosed in parentheses. If reference is made to several papers published in the same year by one author, use the suffixes a, b, c, etc., after the year number (the suffixes being chosen according to the order in which you mention the articles). For example, the text may appear as follows:

Lehenbauer (1914) has investigated the growth of maize seedlings in relation to temperature. Physiological temperature indices have been derived by Livingston (1916a) for the study of plant growth in relation to climatic conditions. Livingston (1916b) has suggested also a single index to represent both moisture and temperature conditions.

When the author's name does not form a part of a sentence in the text, reference to a citation should be made by a parenthesis after an important word or at the end of the sentence. (For example: The optimum temperature for the growth of maize seedlings has been found to be 32°C. (Lehenbauer, 1914). Also: Attention has been directed recently to the relation of plant growth to temperature (Lehenbauer, 1914; Livingston, 1916a, 1916b; Fawcett, 1921).)

14. *Arrangement in bibliography*. The bibliography should be placed at the end of the article. It should

begin on a new sheet of paper; this is necessary to facilitate revision and typesetting. The first sheet should bear the center heading "Literature cited," which will be printed in capitals of the type used for the bibliography.

The citations should be arranged alphabetically, according to authors' names. A number of articles by the same author should be listed in chronological order, according to the year of publication. The author's name should be typewritten flush with the left-hand edge of the writing, and second and succeeding lines should be indented 10 spaces on the typewriter. For example:

LEHENBAUER, P. A. 1914. Growth of maize seedlings in relation to temperature. Physiol. Res. 1: 247–288. 4 fig.

LIVINGSTON, B. E. 1906. The relation of desert plants to soil moisture and to evaporation. Carnegie Inst. Washington Pub. 50: 1–78.

LIVINGSTON, B. E. 1916a. Physiological temperature indices for the study of plant growth in relation to climatic conditions. Physiol. Res. 1: 399–420. 4 fig.

LIVINGSTON, B. E. 1916b. A single climatic index to represent both moisture and temperature conditions as related to plants. Physiol. Res. 1: 421–440. 1 fig.

Journals with numbered volumes

15. *Items and form.* Each citation of an article in a journal should include the following items:

(a) *Name of author.* The surname should be followed by a comma and given names or initials, all in large and small caps. (Underscore with three lines to indicate caps; with two lines to indicate small caps.) Given names or initials should be written as they appear in the article cited. The author's name should be followed by a period. (For example: TOWNSEND, M. R.) If there are several authors, only the name of the first should be inverted.[21] (For example: NOYES, A. A., AND K. G. FALK.)

(*b*) *Year of publication of the article*, followed by a period. (For example: 1910.) If you cite several papers published in the same year by one author, follow the year number by a, b, c, etc. (For example: 1916a, 1916b, 1916c.)

(*c*) *Title of paper*, exactly like the original in wording and punctuation. A period should follow the title even if punctuation is omitted in the original. Only the first word and proper names should have capital initials, except when the title is in Danish, Dutch, or German.

(*d*) *Name of serial publication* (journal, periodical, etc.). Standard abbreviations should be used for the names of serial publications (p. 79).

(*e*) *Volume number*, given in Arabic figures followed by a colon, all in black-face type (indicated by underlining the volume number and colon with a single wavy line).

(*f*) *Page numbers.* The number of the first page of the article should be separated by an en dash (indicated by a hyphen, or, more clearly, by an extra-length hyphen) from the number of the last page.

(*g*) *Number of plates and text figures.* The serial numbers of these are given in Arabic figures. (For example: Pl. 1–5, fig. 1–9. 3 fig. Fig. 1–6.)

BAKER, C. F. 1923. The Jassoidea related to the Stenocotidæ with special reference to Malayan species. Philippine Jour. Sci. **23**: 345–406. Pl. 1–5.

CONN, H. J. 1910. Future methods of soil bacteriological investigations. Centralbl. f. Bakteriol., Parasitenk. u. Infekt.-Krankh. 2: **25**: 454–457. [Note the series number "2."]

[21] In many journals all names are inverted. (For example: NOYES, A. A., AND FALK, K. G.)

DORSET, M., C. N. McBRYDE, W. B. NILES, AND J. H. RIETZ.
1918. Investigations concerning the sources and chan-
nels of infection in hog cholera. Jour. Agric. Res.
13: 101–131.

LIVINGSTON, B. E. 1912. The choosing of a problem for research in plant physiology. Plant World **15**: 73–82.

PARSONS, FLOYD W. May 5, 1923. Pioneering beyond the rim.
Saturday Evening Post **195**[45]: 22–23, 123–125, 129. [Note
that the superscript figure ([45]) following the volume
(**195**) shows that this article appears in number 45 of
volume 195. This method of citation should be used
when each issue, or number, of the periodical begins
with page 1. Also note that the exact date of issue is
given.]

PAVLOV, P. N. 1916. Molecular state of pure liquids. Jour.
Russ. Phys. Chem. Soc. **48**: 1175–1196. *Cited in*
Chem. Absts. **11**: 1583–1584. 1917. [A citation which
is taken from an abstract journal, such as *Chemical
Abstracts*, *Biological Abstracts*, or *Experiment Station
Record*, or from any publication other than the original,
should show clearly the source.]

REINKING, OTTO A. 1918. Philippine economic-plant diseases.
Philippine Jour. Sci., Section A, **13**: 165–274. Pl. 1–22,
fig. 1–43.

Experiment station bulletins

16. *Items and form.* In citing experiment station bulletins and other issues of serial publications bearing an
individual number but no volume number, the bulletin
number should be used like the volume number of a
journal. But the bulletin number should be given in
Roman (not bold-face) type. (For example: Univ.
Illinois Agric. Exper. Sta. Bull. 165: 463–579.) Where
a bulletin or part bears a volume number as well as an
individual number, but is not paged continuously with
other parts, it is customary to cite the volume, in bold-
face, followed by a superscript figure corresponding to
the number of the parts, in light-face type, preceding
the colon that stands before the page reference.

BROWN, WILLIAM H., AND ARTHUR F. FISCHER. 1918. Philip-
pine bamboos. Philippine Bur. Forestry Bull. 15:
1–32. Pl. 1–33.
KELLEY, W. P. 1915. Ammonification and nitrification in
Hawaiian soils. Hawaii Agric. Exper. Sta. Bull. 37:
1–52.
MITCHELL, H. H., AND H. S. GRINDLEY. 1913. The element of
uncertainty in the interpretation of feeding experiments.
Univ. Illinois Agric. Exper. Sta. Bull. 165: 463–579.
Fig. 1–8.

Books

17. *Items and form.* In the citation of a book, the
name of the author, the year of publication (copyright
date), and the title should be given in the same way as
in the citation of a journal article. The remainder of the
book citation departs somewhat from the form described
above. An example will illustrate the form that should
be used in citing a book.

CURTIS, CARLTON C. 1917. Nature and development of plants.
6th ed., vii + 506 p., 342 fig. New York: Henry Holt
and Company.

Note that the edition (6th ed.) is given after the title
of the book. The number of pages (vii + 506 p.) is
given next, the introductory pages (vii) being shown in
Roman numerals (made with small letters, not capitals).
The number of pages is followed by a comma and the
number of figures (342 fig.). Then the place of publication is given, followed by a colon and the name of the
publisher.

BAILEY, L. H. 1921. The principles of vegetable-gardening.
18th ed., xiii + 490 p., 252 fig. New York: Macmillan
Company.
DUFF, A. WILMER (EDITOR). 1910. A text-book of physics.
2nd ed., xi + 698 p., 525 fig. Philadelphia: P. Blakiston's
Son & Company.

KELLEY, TRUMAN L. 1923. Statistical method. xi + 390 p., 24 fig. New York: Macmillan Company.

OLSEN, JOHN C. (EDITOR). 1921. Van Nostrand's chemical annual. 5th issue, xxii + 900 p. New York: D. Van Nostrand Company.

TREADWELL, F. P. 1919. Analytical chemistry. Translation from the German by William T. Hall. Volume II. Quantitative analysis. 5th ed., xi + 940 p., 126 fig. and 1 colored chart. New York: John Wiley & Sons, Inc.

Yearbooks

18. *Items and form.* An example will illustrate the form that should be used for yearbooks:

BACK, E. A. 1918. Danger of introducing fruit flies in tho United States. U. S. Dept. Agric. Yearbook **1917**: 185–196. [Yearbooks are not numbered as volumes, but only by year. The actual time of publication— as shown in the example—is usually one year, but some-times several years, later than that covered by the yearbook.]

FOURTH METHOD

19. *Text reference to footnote citations.* The citations should be given as footnotes, numbered consecutively (from 1 up) throughout each article and indicated by superscript numerals. If other footnotes occur, they should be numbered in the same series with the citations. The superscript reference numeral to each footnote should be placed in the text, after the punctuation mark that follows the word or sentence to which the footnote refers. Indicate the superscript numeral by typewriting it above the line and putting a V-shaped mark under the numeral.

The footnotes should not be inserted in the text, but should be typewritten on separate sheets (as many as

convenient being written on a sheet).[22] Each footnote
should be indented as a paragraph and should be preceded by a superscript numeral corresponding to the
reference number in the text. The sheets bearing footnotes should be put at the end of the text copy, each sheet
bearing the word "Footnotes," inclosed in a circle.
Before the article is printed, each footnote will be inserted at the foot of the proper page.

Journals with numbered volumes

20. *Items and form.* Each citation of an article in a
journal should include the following items:

(*a*) *Surname of author*, followed by a comma.

(*b*) *Abbreviated name of serial publication*, followed by
a comma, all in italic type (indicated by underlining with
a single straight line).

(*c*) *Volume number*, given in black-face Arabic figures
and followed by a comma (indicated by underlining with
a single wavy line).

(*d*) *Number of page cited.*

(*e*) *Year of publication of article*, in parentheses, followed by a period.

[1] Taylor, *Jour. Phys. Chem.*, **30,** 154 (1926).

[2] Thomson, *Philosoph. Mag.*, [7] **3,** 241 (1927). [Note the series
number in square brackets.]

[3] (a) English and Turner, *Proc. Chem. Soc.*, **30,** 162 (1914). (b)
Lange and Dürr, *Ztschr. f. Elektrochemie*, **32,** 85 (1926).

[4] Euler and Bolin, *Ztschr. f. physiol. Chemie*, **57,** 97 (1908);
61, 72 (1909).

[5] Bartolotti, *La Gazetta chim. ital.*, **30** [II], 231 (1900). [Note
the part number in square brackets.]

---

[22] *The Journal of the American Chemical Society* requires each
footnote to be inserted, without a number, as a separate line
(or lines) immediately following the word to which it refers in
the text.

[6] Freundler and Damond, *Compt. rend. Acad. des sci. Paris* **141**, 830 (1905); *Chem. Zentralbl.*, **77** [I], 130 (1906).

Experiment station bulletins

21. *Items and form.* In citing experiment station bulletins and other issues of serial publications bearing an individual number but no volume number, the form shown by the following examples should be used:

[1] Dungan, *Illinois Agric. Exper. Sta. Bull.*, 284, **1926,** p. 254.
[2] Breazeale and Burgess, *Arizona Agric. Exper. Sta. Tech. Bull.*, 6, **1926,** p. 125.
[3] Kelley, *Hawaii Agric. Exper. Sta. Bull.*, 37, **1915,** p. 1.

Books

22. *Items and form.* In citing books, use the form shown by the following examples:

[1] Mellor, "Inorganic and Theoretical Chemistry," Longmans, Green and Co., London, **1923,** vol. 4, pp. 625, 645.
[2] Treadwell, "Analytical Chemistry," translated by Hall, John Wiley and Sons, Inc., New York, **1919,** vol. 2, 5th ed., p. 210.
[3] Clark, "The Determination of Hydrogen Ions," The Williams & Wilkins Co., Baltimore, **1922,** 2nd ed., pp. 101–107.

Yearbooks

23. *Items and form.* An example will illustrate the form that should be used:

[1] Back, *U. S. Dept. Agric. Yearbook,* **1917,** 185 (1918). [Note that this yearbook is for 1917, but it was not published until 1918.]

FORM OF CITATION IN VARIOUS JOURNALS

24. *Miscellaneous examples.* The method of indicating literature references in the text and giving citations differs in details in the various scientific journals. The

forms given above are essentially the same as those employed in many periodicals.   In preparing references the most important thing is to give the citations in detail, so that they include all essential data.   In the final revision you should make the references conform to the precise style employed by the journal in which your article is to be published.   The following examples will serve to illustrate some of the forms used by periodicals.

(1) WESTON, W. H., JR. 1923 Production and dispersal of conidia in the Philippine sclerosporas of maize. *Jour. Agric. Res.* 23: 239–278. [Citations are arranged alphabetically at the end of the article, and are numbered consecutively; they are referred to in the text by numbers in parentheses.]

(1) WESTON, W. H., Jr.
1923. PRODUCTION AND DISPERSAL OF CONIDIA IN THE PHILIPPINE SCLEROSPORAS OF MAIZE. Jour. Agric. Res. 23: 239–278, illus. [Citations are arranged alphabetically at the end of the article, and are numbered consecutively; they are referred to in the text by italic numbers in parentheses.]

[1] Weston, W. H., Jr., Jour. Agric. Res., Washington, **23**, 1923 (239–278). [Citations are numbered consecutively throughout an article and placed at the end of the article; they are referred to in the text by superscript numbers.]

1. WESTON, W. H., JR. Production and dispersal of conidia in the Philippine sclerosporas of maize. Jour. Agric. Res. **23** (1923) 239–278. [Citations are arranged alphabetically at the end of the article, and are numbered consecutively; they are referred to in the text by superscript numbers in parentheses.]

[1] Weston, W. H., Jr., Production and dispersal of conidia in the Philippine sclerosporas of maize. Jour. Agric. Res. **23** (1923) 239–278. [Citations are given in footnotes, numbered consecutively throughout an article.]

1. Weston, W. H., Jr.: Jour. Agric. Res. **23**: 239 (Jan. 27) 1923. [Citations are given in footnotes, numbered consecutively throughout an article.]

ABBREVIATIONS OF NAMES OF PERIODICAL PUBLICATIONS

25. *Rules for abbreviations.* A satisfactory method of writing abbreviated names of periodical publications is shown in the following list. In preparing a bibliography, the author should base his abbreviations upon a careful study of those used by the publication in which his paper is to be printed. A uniform style must be used throughout a single bibliography.

The following rules should be observed in giving abbreviated names of periodical publications: (*a*) Each abbreviated name should be based upon the complete name of the publication, not upon something that resembles it. (*b*) The abbreviations should be self-explanatory, or, at least, clear to those familiar with the literature of science. (*c*) Names of places and persons in titles should not be abbreviated. (*d*) The sequence of the words in the complete title should be followed. (*e*) Prepositions and articles should be omitted when their omission does not lead to obscurity.

AGRICULTURE

American Forestry (Washington)..................Amer. Forestry (Wash.)

American Horticulturist (Detroit, Michigan).....Amer. Horticulturist (Detroit)

American Society of Agronomy. Journal (Washington)....................................Jour. Amer. Soc. Agron. (Wash.)

International Institute of Agriculture. Annuaire international de législation agricole (Rome)....Ann. internat. de légis. agric. (Rome)

International Institute of Agriculture. Bulletin of the Bureau of Economic and Social Intelligence (Rome)................................Bull. Bur. Econ. and Soc. Intell. (Rome)

Journal of Dairy Science (Baltimore)..............Jour. Dairy Sci. (Balt.)

Die landwirtschaftlichen Versuchs-Stationen (Berlin) ....Landwirtsch. Versuchs-Stat. (Berl.)

The Philippine Agriculturist (Los Baños, Philippine Islands)....................................Philippine Agriculturist (Los Baños, P. I.)

Soil Science (Baltimore)...........................Soil Sci. (Balt.)

United States Bureau of Plant Industry. Bulletin
(Washington)....................................U. S. Bur. Plant Indus. Bull.
(Wash.)
United States Bureau of Soils. Bulletin (Wash-
ington)..U. S. Bur. Soils Bull. (Wash.)
United States Department of Agriculture. Ex-
periment Station Record (Washington)........U. S. Dept. Agric. Exper. Sta.
Rec. (Wash.)
United States Department of Agriculture.
Farmers' Bulletin (Washington)...............U. S. Dept. Agric. Farmers'
Bull. (Wash.)
United States Department of Agriculture. Jour-
nal of Agricultural Research (Washington).....Jour. Agric. Res. (Wash.)
United States Department of Agriculture. Year-
book (Washington)..............................U. S. Dept. Agric. Yearbook
(Wash.)
United States Forest Service. Bulletin (Wash-
ington)..U. S. Forest Serv. Bull. (Wash.)

ANTHROPOLOGY

American Anthropologist (Lancaster, Pennsyl-
vania)..Amer. Anthropologist (Lan-
caster, Pa.)
American Journal of Physical Anthropology
(Washington)...................................Amer. Jour. Phys. Anthropol.
(Wash.)
Archiv für Anthropologie (Braunschweig)..........Arch. f. Anthropol. (Braun-
schweig)
Archiv für Rassen- und Gesellschafts-Biologie
(Berlin)..Arch. f. Rassen- u. Gesellsch.-
Biol. (Berl.)
Revue anthropologique (Paris).....................Rev. anthropol. (Paris)
Revue d'ethnographie et des traditions populaires
(Paris)..Rev. d'ethnog. et des trad.
popul. (Paris)
United States Bureau of American Ethnology.
Bulletin (Washington).........................U. S. Bur. Ethnol. Bull. (Wash.)

ASTRONOMY

American Nautical Almanac (Washington)........Amer. Naut. Almanac (Wash.)
The Astronomical Journal (Boston)................Astron. Jour. (Boston)
Astronomische Nachrichten (Kiel)................Astron. Nachrich. (Kiel)
The Astrophysical Journal (Chicago)..............Astrophys. Jour. (Chicago)
Berliner astronomisches Jahrbuch (Berlin)..........Berliner astron. Jahrb. (Berl.)
Bulletin astronomique (Paris).....................Bull. astron. (Paris)
The Nautical Almanac and Astronomical Ephem-
eris (Edinburgh)...............................Naut. Almanac and Astron.
Ephem. (Edinburgh)

L'Observatoire royal de Belgique. Annuaire
(Bruxelles)....................................Ann. l'Observatoire roy. de
Belgique (Bruxelles)

BOTANICAL AND ZOÖLOGICAL SCIENCES

Abstracts of Bacteriology (Baltimore)..............Absts. Bacteriol. (Balt.)
American Journal of Botany (Lancaster, Penn-
sylvania)......................................Amer. Jour. Bot. (Lancaster,
Pa.)
The American Naturalist (New York)..............Amer. Nat. (N. Y.)
Annals of Botany (London).......................Ann. Bot. (Lond.)
L'Année biologique, comptes rendus annuels des
travaux de biologie générale (Paris).............L'Année biol. (Paris)
Archiv für mikroskopische Anatomie und Ent-
wicklungsmechanik (Berlin)....................Arch. f. mikrosk. Anat. u.
Entwickl.-mech. (Berl.)
Archiv für Protistenkunde (Jena)..................Arch. f. Protistenk. (Jena)
Archives d'anatomie microscopique (Paris).........Arch. d'anat. microsc. (Paris)
Archives de morphology générale et expérimentale
(Paris)..Arch. de morphol. gén. et expér.
(Paris)
Archives de zoologie expérimentale et générale
(Paris)..Arch. de zool. expér. et gén.
(Paris)
Archivio di scienze biologiche (Napoli)..............Arch. di sci. biol. (Napoli)
Biometrika (Cambridge, England).................Biometrika (Cambridge, Eng.)
The Botanical Gazette (Chicago)..................Bot. Gaz. (Chicago)
Botanisches Centralblatt (Jena)...................Bot. Centralbl. (Jena)
Le Botaniste (Caen)...............................Le Botaniste (Caen)
Bulletin of the Torrey Botanical Club (Lancaster,
Pennsylvania)................................Bull. Torrey Bot. Club (Lan-
caster, Pa.)
La Cellule (Lierre et Louvain).....................La Cellule (Lierre et Lou-
vain)
Deutsche botanische Gesellschaft, Berlin. Be-
richte (Berlin)................................Ber. Deut. bot. Gesellsch.
(Berl.)
Ecology (Brooklyn, New York)...................Ecology (N. Y.)
Entomological News (Philadelphia)...............Entomol. News (Phila.)
Ergebnisse und Forschungen der Zoologie (Jena)....Ergeb. u. Forsch. d. Zool.
(Jena)
The Eugenics Review (London)...................Eugen. Rev. (Lond.)
Gegenbaurs morphologisches Jahrbuch (Leip-
zig)...Gegenbaurs morphol. Jahrb.
(Leipzig)
Internationale Zeitschrift für physikalisch-
chemische Biologie (Leipzig und Berlin)........Internat. Ztschr. f. physikal.
Biol. (Leipzig u. Berl.)
Journal of Bacteriology (Baltimore)...............Jour. Bacteriol. (Balt.)
The Journal of Ecology (Cambridge, England).....Jour. Ecol. (Cambridge, Eng.)
The Journal of Experimental Zoölogy (Philadel-
phia)..Jour. Exper. Zoöl. (Phila.)

The Journal of General Physiology (New York)....Jour. Gen. Physiol. (N. Y.)
Journal of Genetics (Cambridge, Massachusetts)....Jour.   Genet.   (Cambridge, Mass.)
The Journal of Heredity (Washington).............Jour. Hered. (Wash.)
Journal of Mammalogy (Baltimore)................Jour. Mammal. (Balt.)
Journal of Morphology (Philadelphia).............Jour. Morphol. (Phila.)
Missouri Botanical Garden. Annals (St. Louis, Missouri)...Ann. Missouri Bot. Gard. (St. Louis, Mo.)
New Phytologist (London)..........................New Phytologist (Lond.)
Physiological Reviews (Baltimore)...................Physiol. Rev. (Balt.)
Phytopathology (Ithaca, New York)...............Phytopathology (Ithaca, N. Y.)
Revue générale d'histologie (Paris)................Rev. gén. d'histol. (Paris)
Zeitschrift für Biologie (München und Berlin)......Ztschr. f. Biol. (München u. Berl.)
Zoologischer Anzeiger (Leipzig)....................Zool. Anz. (Leipzig)

ENGINEERING

Archiv für Elektrotechnik (Berlin).................Arch. f. Elektrotech. (Berl.)
The Civil Engineer and Architect's Journal (London).......................................Civ. Engineer and Architect's Jour. (Lond.)
Coal Age (New York).............................Coal Age (N. Y.)
The Electric Journal (Pittsburgh, Pennsylvania)... Elec. Jour. (Pittsburgh, Pa.)
The Electrical Review (London)...................Elec. Rev. (Lond.)
The Electrical World (New York).................Elec. World (N. Y.)
Elektrotechnische Zeitschrift (Berlin).............Elektrotech. Ztschr. (Berl.)
Engineering (London)..............................Engineering (Lond.)
The Engineering and Mining Journal (New York).. Engineer. and Mining Jour. (N. Y.)
The Engineering Index (New York and London)...Engineer. Index (N. Y. and Lond.)
Engineering News (New York)....................Engineer. News (N. Y.)
The Engineering Record, Building Record and Sanitary Engineer (New York)................Engineer. Rec., Build. Rec. and San. Engineer (N. Y.)
Le Génie civil (Paris).............................Le Génie civil (Paris)
The Illuminating Engineer (London)..............Illum. Engineer (Lond.)
International Journal of Public Health (Geneva)...Internat. Jour. Pub. Health (Geneva)
Internationale elektrotechnische Zeitschrift (Wien)..Internat. elektrotech. Ztschr. (Wien)
The Journal of Industrial Hygiene (New York).....Jour. Indust. Hyg. (N. Y.)
Lighting Journal (New York)......................Lighting Jour. (N. Y.)
La Lumière électrique (Paris).....................La Lumière élec. (Paris)
The Mining and Engineering World (Chicago)......Mining and Engineer. World (Chicago)
The Mining Journal (London)......................Mining Jour. (Lond.)

Municipal and County Engineering (Indianapolis,
  Indiana)..Munic. and Co. Engineer.
                                                    (Indianapolis, Ind.)
The Radio Review (London).......................Radio Rev. (Lond.)
Railway Age (New York)..........................Rwy. Age (N. Y.)
Railway Gazette (London)........................Rwy. Gaz. (Lond.)
The Street Railway Journal (New York)...........Street Rwy. Jour. (N. Y.)
La Technique moderne (Paris)....................La Tech. mod. (Paris)
The Technology Review (Boston, Massachusetts)...Technol. Rev. (Boston)
United States Bureau of Standards. Technologic
  Papers (Washington)............................U. S. Bur. Stand. Technol.
                                                    Papers (Wash.)

GEOLOGY AND GEOGRAPHY

The American Mineralogist (Philadelphia)..........Amer. Mineralogist (Phila.)
Annales de paléontologie (Paris)..................Ann. de paléontol. (Paris)
Annales des sciences géologiques (Paris)..........Ann. des sci. géol. (Paris)
L'Année géographique (Paris)......................L'Année géograph. (Paris)
Annuaire géologique universel. Revue de géol-
  ogie et paléontologie (Paris)...................Ann. géol. univers. Rev. de géol
                                                    et paléontol. (Paris)
Beiträge zur Geophysik (Stuttgart)................Beitr. z. Geophysik (Stuttgart)
Bulletins of American Paleontology (Ithaca,
  New York).......................................Bull. Amer. Paleontol. (Ithaca
                                                    N. Y.)
Centralblatt für Mineralogie, Geologie und Palae-
  ontologie (Stuttgart)...........................Centralbl. f. Mineral., Geol. u.
                                                    Palaeontol. (Stuttgart)
Deutsche geologische Gesellschaft (Berlin). Zeit-
  schrift (Berlin)................................Ztschr. Deut. geol. Gesellsch.
                                                    (Berl.)
Economic Geology (New Haven, Connecticut)....Econ. Geol. (New Haven, Conn.)
The Geographical Journal (London)................Geograph. Jour. (Lond.)
The Geographical Review (New York)..............Geograph. Rev. (N. Y.)
Geographisches Jahrbuch (Gotha)..................Geograph. Jahrb. (Gotha)
The Geological Magazine; or Monthly Journal of
  Geology (London)...............................Geol. Mag. (Lond.)
Geologische Rundschau (Leipzig)..................Geol. Rundschau (Leipzig)
Geologische und palaeontologische Abhand-
  lungen (Jena)...................................Geol. u. palaeontol. Abhandl.
                                                    (Jena)
Geologisches Archiv (Königsberg).................Geol. Arch. (Königsberg)
Geologisches Centralblatt (Leipzig and New
  York)...Geol. Centralbl. (Leipzig)
Giornale di geologica pratica (Perugia)...........Giorn. di geol. pratica (Perugia)
The Journal of Geology (Chicago).................Jour. Geol. (Chicago)
Palaeobotanische Zeitschrift (Berlin).............Palaeobot. Ztschr. (Berl.)
Palaeontographica (Stuttgart).....................Palaeontographica (Stuttgart)
Palaeontographical Society, London. Publications
  (London)..Palaeontograph. Soc. London.
                                                    Pub. (Lond.)

Palaeontologische Zeitschrift (Berlin)..............Palaeontol. Ztschr. (Berl.)
The Pan-American Geologist (Des Moines, Iowa)...Pan-Amer.   Geologist   (Des Moines, Iowa)
Petermanns Mitteilungen (Gotha).................Petermanns Mitteil. (Gotha)
Revue critique de paléozoologie (Paris).............Rev. crit. de paléozool. (Paris)
Revue de géologie et des sciences connexes (Liége)..Rev. de géol. et des sci. connexes (Liége)
Schweizerische mineralogische und petrographische Mitteilungen (Frauenfeld)...............Schweizer. mineral. u. petrograph. Mitteil. (Frauenfeld)
The Scottish Geographical Magazine (Edinburgh)..Scottish Geograph. Mag. (Edinburgh)
United States Bureau of Mines. Bulletin (Washington)..U. S. Bur. Mines Bull. (Wash.)
Zeitschrift für Kristallographie (Leipzig)............Ztschr. f. Kristallograph. (Leipzig)

HISTORICAL, ECONOMIC, POLITICAL AND SOCIAL SCIENCES

The American Journal of International Law (New York)...Amer. Jour. Internat. Law (N. Y.)
American Journal of Sociology (Chicago)..........Amer. Jour. Sociol. (Chicago)
The American Political Science Review (Baltimore)...Amer. Polit. Sci. Rev. (Balt.)
Annalen des Deutschen Reichs für Gesetzgebung, Verwaltung und Volkswirtschaft (Berlin).......Ann. d. Deut. Reichs f. Gesetzgeb., Verwalt. u. Volkswirtsch. (Berl.)
The Annalist (New York)..........................Annalist (N. Y.)
L'Année sociologique (Paris)......................L'Année sociol. (Paris)
The Annual Register (London).....................Annual Register (Lond.)
Archiv für die Geschichte des Socialismus und der Arbeiterbewegung (Leipzig)...............Arch. f. d. Gesch. d. Socialismus (Leipzig)
Archiv für Eisenbahnwesen (Berlin)...............Arch. f. Eisenbahnw. (Berl.)
Archiv für Sozialwissenschaft und Sozialpolitik (Tübingen)....................................Arch. f. Sozialwiss. u. Sozialpolit. (Tübingen)
Archives de droit international et de législation comparée (New York).........................Arch. de droit internat. (N. Y.)
The Bankers' Magazine (Baltimore)...............Bankers' Mag. (Balt.)
Blätter für vergleichende Rechtswissenschaft und Volkswirtschaftslehre (Berlin).................Blätter f. vergl. Rechtswiss. u. Volkswirtschaftsl. (Berl.)
The British Year Book of International Law (London)......................................Brit. Year Book Internat. Law (Lond.)
The Commercial and Financial Chronicle (New York)...Commerc. and Finan. Chron. (N. Y.)

Deutsche Zeitschrift für Geschichtswissenschaft
(Freiburg)....................................Deut. Ztschr. f. Geschichts-
wiss. (Freiburg)
The Economist (London)...........................Economist (Lond.)
L'Économiste français (Paris).....................L'Écon. français (Paris)
The Family (New York)............................Family (N. Y.)
Foreign Affairs (New York)........................Foreign Affairs (N. Y.)
Historische Vierteljahrschrift (Freiburg)............Histor. Vierteljahrschr. (Frei-
burg)
Instituts Solvay. Revue de l'Institut de soci-
ologie (Bruxelles)..............................Inst. Solvay. Rev. de l'Inst.
sociol. (Bruxelles)
The International Socialist Review (Chicago)......Internat. Socialist Rev. (Chi-
cago)
Jahrbuch des Völkerrechts (München und Leip-
zig)...Jahrb. des Völkerrechts (Münch-
en u. Leipzig)
The Journal of International Relations (Worcester,
Massachusetts).................................Jour. Internat. Rel. (Worcester,
Mass.)
Journal of Social Science (New York and Boston)...Jour. Social Sci. (N. Y. and
Boston)
Klio. Beiträge zur alten Geschichte (Leipzig).,.,...Klio. (Leipzig)
The New Europe (London)........................New Europe (Lond.)
The Political Quarterly (London)..................Polit. Quart. (Lond.)
Political Science Quarterly (Boston, New York,
and Chicago)...................................Polit. Sci. Quart. (Boston,
N. Y., and Chicago)
Revue historique (Paris)...........................Rev. histor. (Paris)
The Round Table (London).......................Round Table (Lond.)
The Sociological Review (Manchester, England)....Sociol. Rev. (Manchester, Eng.)
The Survey (New York)...........................Survey (N. Y.)
Zeitschrift für Politik (Berlin)......................Ztschr. f.Polit. (Berl.)

MATHEMATICS

American Journal of Mathematics (Baltimore)......Amer. Jour. Math. (Balt.)
The American Mathematical Monthly (Lancaster,
Pennsylvania, and Providence, Rhode Island).Amer. Math. Month. (Lancas-
ter, Pa., and Providence,
R. I.)
American Mathematical Society, New York.
Bulletin (Lancaster, Pennsylvania, and New
York)..Bull. Amer. Math. Soc. (Lan-
caster, Pa., and N. Y.)
American Mathematical Society, New York.
Transactions (Lancaster, Pennsylvania, and
New York).....................................Trans. Amer. Math. Soc. (Lan-
caster, Pa., and N. Y.)
Annali di matematica pura ed applicata (Mi-
lano)...Ann. di matem. pura ed appli-
cata (Milano)

Annals of Mathematics (Charlottesville, Virginia)...Ann. Math. (Charlottesville, Va.)

Journal de mathématiques pures et appliquées (Paris)...Jour. de math. pures et appliquées (Paris)

Mathematische Annalen (Leipzig)..................Math. Ann. (Leipzig)

The Quarterly Journal of Pure and Applied Mathematics (London)................................Quart. Jour. Pure and Applied Math. (Lond.)

MEDICINE

American Journal of Diseases of Children (Chicago)..Amer. Jour. Dis. Child. (Chicago)

The American Journal of Hygiene (Baltimore).....Amer. Jour. Hyg. (Balt.)

American Journal of Physiological Optics (Southbridge, Massachusetts)..........................Amer. Jour. Physiol. Optics (Southbridge, Mass.)

American Journal of Physiology (Baltimore).......Amer. Jour. Physiol. (Balt.)

The American Journal of Psychiatry (formerly The American Journal of Insanity) (Baltimore)...Amer. Jour. Psychiatry (formerly Amer. Jour. Insanity) (Balt.)

The American Journal of the Medical Sciences (Philadelphia and New York)..................Amer. Jour. Med. Sci. (Phila. and N. Y.)

The American Journal of Tropical Medicine (Baltimore)....................................Amer. Jour. Trop. Med. (Balt.)

American Medical Association. Journal (Chicago).Jour. Amer. Med. Assoc. (Chicago)

The Anatomical Record (Philadelphia).............Anat. Rec. (Phila.)

Annales des maladies des organes génito-urinaires (Paris)...Ann. des malad. des org. génito-urin. (Paris)

Annals of Clinical Medicine (Baltimore)............Ann. Clin. Med. (Balt.)

Archiv für Frauenkunde und Eugenetik (Würzburg)...Arch. f. Frauenk. u. Eugenetik (Würzburg)

Archiv für Kinderheilkunde (Stuttgart)............Arch. f. Kinderheilk. (Stuttgart)

Archiv für wissenschaftliche und practische Thierheilkunde (Berlin)................................Arch. f. wissensch. u. pract. Thierheilk. (Berl.)

Archives de gynécologie et de tocologie (Paris).....Arch. de gynécol. et de tocol. (Paris)

Archives de médecine des enfants (Paris)...........Arch. de méd. des enfants (Paris)

Archives de médecine expérimentale et d'anatomie pathologique (Paris)......................Arch. de méd. expér. et d'anat. pathol. (Paris)

Archives of Neurology and Psychiatry (Chicago)...Arch. Neurol. and Psychiatry (Chicago)

Archives of Occupational Therapy (Baltimore).....Arch. Occup. Therapy (Balt.)

The British Journal of Children's Diseases (London)...Brit. Jour. Child. Dis. (Lond.)

The British Journal of Experimental Pathology (London and Toronto)........................Brit. Jour. Exper. Pathol. (Lond. and Toronto)

Centralblatt für Bakteriologie, Parasitenkunde und Infektionskrankheiten (Jena).............Centralbl. f. Bakteriol., Parasitenk. u. Infekt.-Krankh. (Jena)

Deutsche Chirurgie (Stuttgart).....................Deut. Chirurgie (Stuttgart)

Deutsche medizinische Wochenschrift (Leipzig).....Deut. med. Wochenschr. (Leipzig)

Deutsche Zeitschrift für Thiermedicin und vergleichende Pathologie (Leipzig)................Deut. Ztschr. f. Thiermedicin u. vergl. Pathol. (Leipzig)

Endocrinology (Glendale, California)..............Endocrinology (Glendale, Calif.)

Folia haematologica (Leipzig).....................Folia haematol. (Leipzig)

Hygienisches Zentralblatt (Leipzig)................Hyg. Zentralbl. (Leipzig)

Index Medicus (New York).........................Index Medicus (N. Y.)

Journal of Cancer Research (Baltimore)...........Jour. Cancer Res. (Balt.)

The Journal of Experimental Medicine (New York)..Jour. Exper. Med. (N. Y.)

The Journal of Immunology (Baltimore)..........Jour. Immunol. (Balt.)

The Journal of Medical Research (Boston, Massachusetts)......................................Jour. Med. Res. (Boston)

The Journal of Pathology and Bacteriology (Cambridge, England)..............................Jour. Path. and Bacteriol. (Cambridge, Eng.)

The Journal of Pharmacology and Experimental Therapeutics (Baltimore).....................Jour. Pharmacol. and Exper. Therap. (Balt.)

Journal of Urology (Baltimore)...................Jour. Urol. (Balt.)

Medicine (Baltimore)..............................Medicine (Balt.)

Medizinisch-naturwissenschaftliches Archiv (Berlin und Wien)..................................Med.-naturwissensch. Arch. (Berl. u. Wien)

Monatsschrift für Geburtshülfe und Gynäkologie (Berlin).......................................Monatsschr. f. Geburtsh. u. Gynäkol. (Berl.)

Le Névraxe (Louvain)..............................Le Névraxe (Louvain)

Nouvelles archives d'obstétrique et de gynécologie (Paris)..................................Nouv. arch. d'obstét. et de gynécol. (Paris)

La Pediatria (Napoli)..............................La Pediatria (Napoli)

Revue de chirurgie (Paris)........................Rev. de chirurgie (Paris)

Revue d'hygiène et de police sanitaire (Paris)......Rev. d'hyg. et de police sanitaire (Paris)

Spezielle Pathologie und Therapie (Wien).........Spez. Pathol. u. Therap. (Wien)

Surgery, Gynecology and Obstetrics (Chicago)....Surg., Gynecol. and Obstet. (Chicago)

Therapeutische Halbmonatshefte (Berlin).........Therap. Halbmonatsh. (Berl.)

Virchows Archiv für pathologische Anatomie und Physiologie und für klinische Medizin (Berlin).Virchows Arch. f. pathol. Anat. (Berl.)

Zeitschrift für Immunitätsforschung und experimentelle Therapie (Jena)......................Ztschr. f. Immunitätsforsch. u. exper. Therap. (Jena)

PHILOSOPHY AND PSYCHOLOGY

The American Journal of Psychology (Worcester, Massachusetts)................................Amer. Jour. Psychol. (Worcester, Mass.)

L'Année philosophique (Paris)......................L'Année philosoph. (Paris)

Archives of Psychology (New York)................Arch. Psychol. (N. Y.)

Behavior Monographs (Baltimore)................Behavior Monogr. (Balt.)

Bibliothek für Philosophie (Berlin)................Bibliothek f. Philosoph. (Berl.)

The British Journal of Psychology (Cambridge, England, and New York)......................Brit. Jour. Psychol. (Cambridge, Eng., and N. Y.)

Fortschritte der Psychologie und ihrer Anwendungen (Leipzig)................................Fortsch. d. Psychol. u. ihrer Anwend. (Leipzig)

International Journal of Ethics (Philadelphia)......Internat. Jour. Ethics (Phila.)

Jahrbuch der Psychoanalyse (Leipzig und Wien)..Jahrb. d. Psychoanalyse (Leipzig u. Wien)

Jahrbuch für Philosophie und phänomenologische Forschung (Halle a. d. Saale)...................Jahrb. f. Philosoph. u. phänomenol. Forschung (Halle a. d. Saale)

Journal de psychologie (Paris)......................Jour. de psychol. (Paris)

Journal für Psychologie und Neurologie (Leipzig)..Jour. f. Psychol. u. Neurol. (Leipzig)

The Journal of Animal Behavior (Cambridge, Massachusetts)................................Jour. Animal Behavior (Cambridge, Mass.)

The Journal of Applied Psychology (Baltimore)....Jour. Applied Psychol. (Balt.)

The Journal of Comparative Neurology (Philadelphia)...Jour. Compar. Neurol. (Phila.)

The Journal of Comparative Psychology (Baltimore)...Jour. Compar. Psychol. (Balt.)

Journal of Personnel Research (Baltimore).........Jour. Personnel Res. (Balt.)

Logos. Internationale Zeitschrift für Philosophie der Kultur (Tübingen)........................Logos (Tübingen)

Mind (London)....................................Mind (Lond.)

The Monist (Chicago)..............................Monist (Chicago)

The Philosophical Review (Boston, Massachusetts).Philosoph. Rev. (Boston)

Philosophische Monatshefte (Berlin)...............Philosoph. Monatsh. (Berl.)

The Psychological Clinic (Philadelphia)...........Psychol. Clin. (Phila.)

The Psychological Index (New York).............Psychol. Index (N. Y.)
The Psychological Review (Lancaster, Pennsylvania)..Psychol. Rev. (Lancaster, Pa.)
Revue philosophique de la France et de l'étranger (Paris)...Rev. philosoph. de la France et de l'étranger (Paris)
La Revue psychologique (Bruxelles)...............La Rev. psychol. (Bruxelles)
Zeitschrift für Philosophie und philosophische Kritik (Leipzig)................................Ztschr. f. Philos. u. philos. Krit. (Leipzig)
Zeitschrift für Psychologie und Physiologie der Sinnesorgane (Hamburg und Leipzig).........Ztschr. f. Psychol. u. Physiol d. Sinnesorg. (Hamburg und Leipzig)

PHYSICS AND CHEMISTRY

The Analyst (London)............................Analyst (Lond.)
Annalen der Physik (Leipzig)......................Ann. d. Physik (Leipzig)
Annales de chimie analytique et Revue de chimie analytique réunies (Paris)......................Ann. de chimie analyt. (Paris)
Annales de physique (Paris).......................Ann. de physique (Paris)
Chemical Abstracts (Easton, Pennsylvania)........Chem. Absts. (Easton, Pa.)
The Chemical News and Journal of Physical Science, with which is incorporated the Chemical Gazette (London)...................Chem. News (Lond.)
Chemiker-Zeitung (Coethen)......................Chemiker-Ztg. (Coethen)
Chemisches Zentralblatt (Berlin)..................Chem. Zentralbl. (Berl.)
Elektrochemische Zeitschrift (Berlin und Schöneberg)..Elektrochem. Ztschr. (Berl. u. Schöneberg)
Fortschritte der Chemie, Physik und physikalischen Chemie (Leipzig).......................Fortsch. d. Chemie, Physik u. physikal. Chemie (Leipzig)
La Gazetta chimica italiana (Roma)...............La Gazetta chim. ital. (Roma)
Journal de chimie physique, électrochimie, thermochimie, radiochimie, mécanique chimique, stoechiométrie (Genève)........................Jour. de chimie physique, electrochimie [etc.] (Genève)
Journal de physique théorique et appliquée (Paris)...Jour. de physique théorique et appliquée (Paris)
The Journal of Analytical and Applied Chemistry (Easton, Pennsylvania).........................Jour. Analyt. and Applied Chem. (Easton, Pa.)
The Journal of Biological Chemistry (New York)...Jour. Biol. Chem. (N. Y.)
Justus Liebig's Annalen der Chemie (Heidelberg)..Liebig's Annalen (Heidelberg)
Optical Society of America. Journal (Philadelphia)...Jour. Optical Soc. Amer. (Phila.)
The Physical Review (Lancaster, Pennsylvania, and Ithaca, New York).......................Phys. Rev. (Lancaster, Pa., and Ithaca, N. Y.)

Physikalische Zeitschrift (Leipzig)..................Physikal. Ztschr. (Leipzig)

Zeitschrift für analytische Chemie (Wiesbaden)....Ztschr. f. analyt. Chemie (Wiesbaden)

Zeitschrift für angewandte Chemie und Zentralblatt für technische Chemie (Leipzig)..........Ztschr. f. angewandte Chemie (Leipzig)

Zeitschrift für Elektrochemie und angewandte physikalische Chemie (Halle)..................Ztschr. f. Elektrochemie [etc.] (Halle)

Zeitschrift für physikalische Chemie, Stöchiometrie und Verwandtschaftslehre (Leipzig)...Ztschr. f. physikal. Chemie [etc.] (Leipzig)

SCIENCE IN GENERAL

Académie des sciences, Paris. Comptes rendus (Paris)...Compt. rend. Acad. des sci. Paris (Paris)

American Academy of Arts and Sciences, Boston. Proceedings (Boston)...........................Proc. Amer. Acad. Arts and Sci. (Boston)

The American Journal of Science (New Haven, Connecticut)...................................Amer. Jour. Sci. (New Haven, Conn.)

American Philosophical Society, Philadelphia. Proceedings (Philadelphia).....................Proc. Amer. Philosoph. Soc. (Phila.)

British Association for the Advancement of Science. Report (London)....................Rept. Brit. Assoc. Adv. Sci. (Lond.)

Carnegie Institution of Washington. Publications (Washington)....................................Carnegie Inst. Washington Pub. (Wash.)

The Dublin Journal of Science (London and Edinburgh).....................................Dublin Jour. Sci. (Lond. and Edinburgh)

Göttingische gelehrte Anzeigen (Berlin)............Göttingische gel. Anz. (Berl.)

R. Istituto lombardo di scienze e lettere, Milan. Rendiconti (Milano)............................Rend. R. Istituto lombardo di sci. e lettere (Milano)

R. Istituto veneto de scienze, lettere ed arti. Atti (Venezia)...................................Atti R. Istituto veneto de sci., lettere ed arti (Venezia)

The London, Edinburgh, and Dublin Philosophical Magazine and Journal of Science (London)..Philosoph. Mag. (Lond.)

National Academy of Sciences, Washington. Proceedings (Washington)...........................Proc. Nat. Acad. Sci. (Wash.)

Nature (London)....................................Nature (Lond.)

Neue Heidelberger Jahrbücher (Heidelberg)........Neue Heidelberger Jahrb. (Heidelberg)

New York Academy of Sciences. Annals (New
    York)..Ann. New York Acad. Sci.
                                                                        (N. Y.)
The Philippine Journal of Science (Manila, Philip-
    pine Islands)...................................Philippine Jour. Sci. (Manila,
                                                                        P. I.).
Revue scientifique (Paris)...........................Rev. scientifique (Paris)
Royal Canadian Institute. Transactions (To-
    ronto)...Trans. Roy. Canadian Inst.
                                                                        (Toronto)
Royal Irish Academy. Proceedings (Dublin).....Proc. Roy. Irish Acad. (Dublin)
Royal Society of Edinburgh. Transactions (Edin-
    burgh)...Trans. Roy. Soc. Edinburgh
                                                                        (Edinburgh)
Royal Society of London. Proceedings (London)..Proc. Roy. Soc. London (Lond.)
Sächsische Akademie der Wissenschaften, Leip-
    zig. Mathematisch-physische Classe. Ab-
    handlungen (Leipzig)...........................Abhandl. Sächsische Akad. d.
                                                                        Wissensch. Leipzig. Math.-
                                                                        phys. Classe. (Leipzig)
Science (New York)................................Science (N. Y.)
Science Abstracts (London and New York)........Sci. Absts. (Lond. and N. Y.)
Science Progress in the Twentieth Century
    (London).......................................Sci. Prog. Twentieth Cent.
                                                                        (Lond.)
The Science Year Book (London).................Sci. Year Book (Lond.)
Scientia, Rivista di scienza (Bologna, Paris,
    and London)...................................Scientia (Bologna)
Scientific American (New York)....................Scientific Amer. (N. Y.)
The Scientific Monthly (New York)................Scientific Month. (N. Y.)
Smithsonian Institution. Annual Report
    (Washington)...................................Smithsonian Inst. Ann. Rept.
                                                                        (Wash.)

ABSTRACTS AND QUOTATIONS

ABSTRACTS

1. *Form.* Reference to a cited publication usually
should be made in the form of an indirect quotation or a
brief abstract that summarizes the discussion presented
in the original publication. (See "Summary," p. 21.)

2. *Credit.* Always give credit for ideas taken directly
from any publication.

3. *Citation.* A citation of each article mentioned must
appear in your bibliography or in a footnote.

4. *Punctuation*. Indirect quotations should not be inclosed in quotation marks.

QUOTATIONS

5. *Form*. When direct quotations are needed, they should be inclosed in quotation marks, and should reproduce the exact words of the original publication, including all details of spelling, capitalization, and punctuation. Corrections or remarks inserted by the one who quotes must be placed in square brackets [ ]. Omissions must be indicated, by a series of four periods. The author should compare carefully the typewritten copy with the original printed matter; this should be done each time the manuscript is copied.

6. *Short quotations*. A short quotation usually should not appear as a separate paragraph. It should be inclosed in quotation marks, and included in a paragraph of your manuscript.

7. *Long quotations*. A quotation of more than five or six lines should be given as a separate paragraph. In the manuscript a quotation of this kind should be inclosed in quotation marks. The publisher usually will omit the quotation marks and print the quotation in smaller type than that used for the text. Each long quotation should be typewritten upon one or more separate sheets of paper that are numbered consecutively with the text pages. The method of preparing the copy is as follows: When the place is reached where a long quotation occurs, remove the text sheet from the typewriter and begin the quotation upon a separate sheet numbered as a new page. Finish typewriting the quotation, using as many sheets as necessary and numbering them as manuscript pages. Then put a new sheet of paper in the typewriter, and continue with the text.

The reason for using this method is that it allows the article to be composed economically on the typesetting machine, which will not set two different sizes of type in one operation. When the manuscript is not prepared in this way, it is necessary for the compositor to handle all of the copy twice, thus causing needless waste of valuable time.

It is a good plan to mark clearly the sheets bearing quotations; this may be done by writing the word "Quotation," inclosed in a circle, in the upper left-hand corner.

8. *Quotation within a quotation.* Use single quotation marks for a quotation within a quotation.

ACKNOWLEDGMENTS

Acknowledgments of help received from others should be made with simplicity and tact. An effusive acknowledgment may be very embarrassing to your critic or adviser. It is fitting, of course, that mention be made of suggestions, criticisms, or other forms of help that you have received, but this should be done in an appropriate way. The form of acknowledgment and its place in the paper should be determined by the usual practice in your college or in the journal in which you expect your article to be published.[23] In general it is a good plan to have the acknowledgment appear in the introduction of the article, in a paragraph in which you refer to the time and place of your work.

[23] Acknowledgment may be made by a brief statement appearing in a footnote to the title of the article. The form is "Prepared in the Department of —————————, under the direction of Professor —————————." If persons other than the adviser have helped, mention of the fact may be made in the form of footnotes in the parts of the paper concerned.

PREPARATION OF AN ANALYTICAL TABLE OF CONTENTS

1. *Analytical outline.* Before a manuscript is offered for publication, an analytical outline, or table of contents, should be prepared. The outline is of advantage in two ways: (*a*) It aids you in making the final revisions of your paper, especially in preparing correct headlines. (*b*) It is almost indispensable to anyone reading your manuscript with the object of criticizing it.

2. *Form of outline.* The outline which follows will serve as an example of an analytical table of contents. The rank of headings for the various divisions of an article should be indicated in the table of contents by graded indentations. It will be noted that the principal divisions are begun flush with the left-hand edge of the writing. The subdivisions of the principal divisions are indented 5 spaces on the typewriter. Smaller subdivisions are indented 10 spaces.

Indicate properly the comparative values of the topics. If two topics logically are coördinate, do not make one topic subordinate to the other. Do not give equal value to two topics if one logically is subordinate to the other.

Example of analytical table of contents

CONTENTS

HEADINGS IN THE TEXT OF AN ARTICLE

1. *Use of outline in revising headings.* The analytical outline, prepared as described above, should be used as a basis for revising, if necessary, the headings that appear in the text of your article, and for indicating the rank of the headings. The editor will mark the manuscript to indicate the sizes and styles of type for headings.

2. *Indication of center headings in text.* In the text, or body of the article, the headings indicating principal divisions of the article should be typewritten in capitals as center headings. In the margin opposite each of these main headings write "Center head" and inclose this in a circle. In the example, "Introduction," "Materials and methods," "Experiments and results," "Discussion of results," "Summary," and "Literature cited" indicate the headings of the main sections of the paper. As a rule, omit the heading "Introduction."

3. *Indication of center subheadings in text.* The headings indicating subdivisions should be typewritten as center headings in small (lower-case) letters; only the first word and proper nouns should have capital initials. In the margin opposite each write "Subhead" and inclose this in a circle. In the sample outline, "Plants," "Cultural methods," "Measurement of climatic conditions," etc., indicate the center subheads.

4. *Indication of paragraph side headings.* Still smaller

subdivisions should appear as side heads, indented as paragraphs. The side head is "run in"—that is, run together in a continuous line with the paragraph to which it belongs. Only the first word and proper nouns should have capital initials. A single straight line should be drawn under each side head to indicate that it is to be printed in italics; a period should follow the side head. In the example, "Temperature," "Rainfall," and "Evaporation" indicate the paragraph side heads.

5. *Over-minute subdivision.* Excessive subdivision of the text should be avoided, since it confuses rather than aids the reader; three grades (center heads, center subheads, and paragraph side heads) are enough.

In a thesis and in the early drafts of an article, it always is desirable to show clearly the principal divisions and their subdivisions, and so these three grades of headings usually are required. In making the final revision for publication, try to avoid the use of center subheads; let the main divisions of the article appear as center heads, and the subdivisions appear as paragraph side heads.

6. *Styles of type for center headings.* As a rule, the author should not mark the manuscript to indicate the styles of type for center headings, unless he is preparing copy ready for the printer. The author should indicate only the rank of the headings, as suggested above. The following outline summarizes a style often used. This style has the advantages of being pleasing to the eye, and economical because composed with the text, in one operation.

CENTER HEADINGS (SMALL CAPS OF TEXT TYPE)

Center subheads (lower-case italics of text type)

PROOF READING

1. *Galley proofs.* Galley proofs, on sheets about 18 cm. wide and 60 cm. long, usually are submitted to the author. The author is expected to correct the proofs; he should see that the proofs agree with the manuscript, and should correct all genuine errors. The proofs should be returned to the editor as soon as possible.

2. *Marks.* All corrections must be made by means of proof-reader's marks in the *margins* of the proof sheets. Corrections should be made clearly and neatly, in ink, if feasible. They should be made horizontally on the page, and opposite the printed lines in which the errors occur.

METHOD

3. *Two persons.* If possible, have another person slowly read aloud from the manuscript, while you follow the galley proofs and make the necessary corrections and changes. The one who reads aloud should call your attention to every paragraph, mark of punctuation, capitalized word, italicized figure or word, bold-face figure or word, etc. If you can not secure the services of another person in this work, then it will be necessary for you carefully to compare the galley proofs with the manuscript, line by line or sentence by sentence.

4. *Two readings.* Always read the proofs *twice*, at least.

MISCELLANEOUS SUGGESTIONS

5. *Special attention.* Give particular attention to tables, figures, names, quotations, and citations. Assume that errors are present; find and correct them.

6. *Questions.* Be sure to answer questions, or queries, made by the printer.

Cancellation

ℰ   Delete, or take out, character or ~~the~~ word marked.

Insertion

the/   Insert ∧ word, letter, or punctuation mark written in the margin.

Spacing

\#   Insert space between∧words, letters, or lines.

◡   Close u͡p, or take out the space.

⊝   Close ͡up, but leave some space.

Position

◎   Tur͓n a reversed letter.

[[Carry farther to the left.

]   C͔arry farther to the right.

⌣   ⌊Move⌋ down a letter, character, or word.

⌐¬   ⌐Move¬ up a letter, character, or word.

□   ∧Indent one em.

=   Straigh͟ten a crooked line.

| | Straighten lateral margin of printing.

tr.   Transpose ⌈of order⌉ words ⌈no⌉ letters.

∨ ∨   Correct∨uneven ∨spacing.

Paragraphing

¶   ∧Make a new paragraph.

no¶   ͡No paragraph.

Miscellaneous

↓   Push down a space or quadrat that prints.

⑦   Question to author.   I͟s͟ ͟t͟h͟i͟s͟ ͟r͟i͟g͟h͟t͟?

stet   Allow to ~~stand~~ as it is.

Kinds of type

l. c.	Put in lower case.
caps	Put in ~~capitals.~~
u	~~u~~se a capital.
s.c.	~~Put~~ in small capitals.
ut	~~Put~~ in small capitals.
rom.	Put in ~~Roman.~~
ital.	Put in ~~italic.~~
b.f.	Put in ~~bold-face.~~
ℓ	Put in **bold-face.**
w. f.	Wrong font (wrong size or style).
⊘	Superscript *1.*
⋁	Superscript *1.*
⋀2	Subscript *2.*
✕	Type is broken or imperfect.

Punctuation

⊙	Period.
⸴/	Comma.
;/	Semicolon.
⊖	Colon.
⋁	Apostrophe.
⸲⸲/ ⸰⸰/	Quotation marks.
–/	Hyphen (-).
en/	One-en dash (–).
$\frac{1}{m}$/	One-em dash (—).
$\frac{2}{m}$/	Two-em dash (——).
(/)	Parentheses.
[/]	Brackets.

7. *Instructions to printer.* If you do not know how to indicate a correction, simply draw a horizontal line through the word that needs to be changed and then write clear instructions in the margin, inclosing the instructions in a circle.

8. *Omissions.* Watch for words or lines that may have been omitted.

9. *Reading for meaning.* After you have read the proofs *twice*, as suggested above, it is well to read them a *third* time, paying particular attention to the sense, or meaning, of the statements. You will not be permitted to make revisions; but genuine errors must be corrected, of course, whenever they are discovered.

10. *Headings.* Look through the proofs for the purpose of correcting errors in all headings.

11. *Expense of alterations.* Alterations, or changes from the original copy sent to the printer, are very expensive, and some journals charge them to the author.

PAGE PROOFS

12. *Steps in printing.* After the corrected galley proofs have been received by the editor and have been read and marked by him, they are returned to the printer. The corrections marked on the galley proofs are made, and then the type is divided into pages of the required length. Page proofs are sent to the editor, who compares them with the galley proofs to see that all the corrections have been made. The editor then reads the page proofs critically, searching for inconsistencies or errors. The page proofs are returned to the printer, who makes the necessary changes and begins the actual press work.

ILLUSTRATIONS

DRAWINGS

1. *Methods of reproduction.* Drawings usually are reproduced by means of zinc etchings, or by the more expensive half-tone and photo-gelatine processes. As a rule, drawings should be prepared in a way that will allow them to be reproduced by zinc etchings.

2. *Paper and ink.* A pure white paper or cardboard (Bristol board) and black, water-proof India ink should be used in preparing the drawings.

3. *Shading.* For reproduction by zinc etchings, any shading that is desired should be done by means of dots or black lines. Very fine shading or extremely small dots can not be reproduced by this process. Dots and lines should be clear and distinct. If they are placed too close together, they may blur when the drawing is reduced in size. Many of the best drawings are mere outlines, made with very few, carefully chosen lines; elaborate drawings rarely are necessary.

If it is essential to show extremely fine details, as in some cytological work, very delicate shading may be done with diluted India ink, and the drawings can be reproduced by the half-tone process or the photo-gelatine process (p. 105). Wash and brush drawings can be reproduced in the same way.

4. *Plates and text figures.* Drawings may be used either as plates or as text figures. Plates are printed on special paper as separate pages and frequently appear at the end of the article. Text figures are printed on the same paper as the text and often have text material above or below them. The appearance of the page is best if every text figure has the same width as the type page.

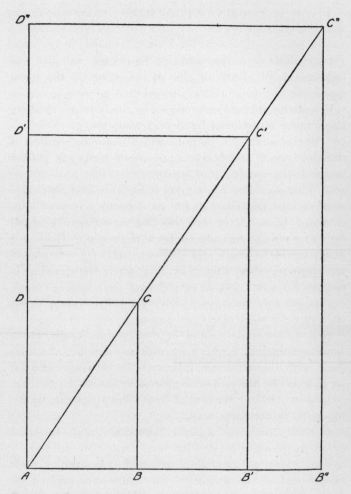

DIAGRAM SHOWING METHOD OF SECURING CORRECT PROPORTIONS
FOR AN ILLUSTRATION

5. *Size of drawing.* The original drawing should be made about two or three times the size of the desired reproduction. The drawing should be made in the right proportions of width and length. Use standard enlargements for drawings, so as to insure ready comparability.

6. *Correct proportions.* A useful method of securing the correct proportions for a page-size plate is illustrated by the accompanying diagram. On a large sheet of drawing paper construct, in pencil, a rectangle $ABCD$ which is the size of the desired reproduction; this usually is the same width as the type page, but is somewhat shorter, to allow space for the legend. Extend the diagonal AC as far as you wish on the paper. Any point on the diagonal will determine a rectangle that has the correct proportions of width and length. For example, the point C' determines the correct rectangle $AB'C'D'$; the point C'' determines the rectangle $AB''C''D''$, etc.

7. *Figure numbers and explanatory letters.* Letters and numbers should be neat, and large enough to be legible when reduced. In the reproduction the letters and numbers should be about one-sixteenth of an inch high. It is best to use printed characters, or to write them in pencil and have them inked in by a draftsman.[24]

Capital and lower-case letters (both usually italic) are used to designate points, lines, objects, etc., in figures; and italic type is used when reference to such letters is made in the text (see p. 38).

8. *Arrangement of figures in plate.* Each plate may include several figures. For reproduction by zinc etchings, the separate drawings should be trimmed and

[24] No skill is required to make neat letters and figures with the aid of the lettering guides made by the Wood-Regan Instrument Co., Inc., of South Orange, N. J.

arranged carefully within a rectangle drawn in pencil on a sheet of stiff white cardboard. The trimmed edges and slight irregularities in the background do not appear in zinc etchings. The size and proportions of the rectangle should be determined as described above. When the best arrangement has been secured, the figures should be pasted to the cardboard, using colorless paste that will neither discolor nor wrinkle the paper. Figure numbers (Arabic, vertical) and explanatory letters should be pasted in proper places, and the rectangle may be drawn in India ink as a border for the plate, or it may be erased if no border be desired. Care should be taken to have the *printed* figures or letters set "straight" and duly separated from drawings.

Regarding the trimming and mounting of drawings *for half-tone reproduction*, see also p. 105.

9. *Diagrams as text figures.* Diagrammatic drawings should be used as text figures, printed, if possible, on the page in which they are mentioned in the text.

see also p. 105.

GRAPHS

10. *Paper and ink.* Graphs are reproduced by zinc etchings, and should be made with black, water-proof India ink on white paper or tracing cloth, or on coördinate paper or cloth, ruled with blue lines. In reproduction the blue lines will be "screened out," leaving only the black ink lines. Any coördinate lines that you wish to appear in the reproduction must be drawn in black ink. Observed points always should show clearly on the graphs.

11. *Unsatisfactory paper.* Coördinate papers ruled with green, black, red, or yellow lines are unsatisfactory unless it is desired that all lines should reproduce. If the coördinate lines are to appear, special care should

be taken to use a paper in which they contrast sharply with the white background.

12. *Size and proportions.* The suggestions made above regarding size and proportions of drawings apply also to graphs.

13. *Graphs as text figures.* Graphs should be used as text figures, printed near the place where reference is made to them. If necessary, a graph may occupy a full page.

PHOTOGRAPHS

14. *Copy.* Photographs are reproduced as half-tones, in which the picture is broken up into minute dots. The photograph for copy should be a perfect print with glossy finish, with fine details and rather pronounced contrasts. It should be flat, and preferably neither trimmed nor mounted.[25] If it is necessary to write on the back of a photograph, use a soft pencil and apply little pressure; otherwise, the writing may show on the face of the print. All wash and brush drawings intended for photographic reproduction should be drawn upon white or blue-white paper, never upon paper with a cream or yellow tint. When mounting is necessary, care always should be taken to use a colorless paste; glue or mucilage often discolors a photograph, and such discoloration will appear in the half-tone.

If a number of separate drawings or photographs are to be arranged together for half-tone reproduction in a single plate, they should be trimmed and mounted with special care. Unless their edges are straight, it will be necessary to have the background routed out, thus doubling or trebling the cost of reproduction. If possible,

[25] Some publishers require photographs to be mounted on flat sheets or cards of standard size.

the drawings or photographs should be fitted together perfectly, so as to cover completely the cardboard on which they are mounted.

15. *Number and reduction.* The plate number or figure number, clear directions for reduction, the author's name and address, and the title of the article should be written on a piece of paper and attached securely with mucilage to the lower margin of the copy for the plate or figure.

16. *Legends.* The legends, or titles, of plates and figures should be self-explanatory. They should be typewritten in numerical order upon one or more sheets of paper, placed at the end of the manuscript following the bibliography. Always supply a short title for the illustration. Any descriptive matter should follow directly after this title, in the form of paragraphs.

The legend of each text figure is printed below the figure. A short title appears below each plate, and complete descriptions of all plates usually are given in a separate section of the paper, following the bibliography and preceding the plates.

17. *Place of insertion.* The place of insertion of each text figure must be marked in the manuscript and in the galley proof. (For example: In the margin write "Insert fig. 2.")

18. *Reference in text.* In the text, the figures and plates should be referred to by number; the words *figure* and *plate* should not be capitalized. Text figures should be numbered from 1 up in each article. Plates should be numbered 1, 2, 3, etc., in each article; and figures in plates should be numbered from 1 up, beginning a new series in each plate. (For example: Examination of

figure 5 of plate 3 shows that . . . .)[26] If the reference is made parenthetically, the words *figure* and *plate* should be abbreviated, using the forms "fig." and "pl." for singular and plural. (For example: The data of table 7 are shown as graphs in figure 4, in which the method of plotting is the same as for series I (fig. 1).)

BIBLIOGRAPHY

ANONYMOUS: A manual of style. 1925. 8th ed., ix + 391 p. Chicago: University of Chicago Press.

ANONYMOUS: Preparation of copy. Bot. Gaz., 1916, lxi, 337-340.

ANONYMOUS: Suggestions to authors. Bur. Sci., Philippine Islands, Press Bull. 58

ALLDUTT, T. C.: Notes on the composition of scientific papers. 1905. 164 p. London: Macmillan and Company.

BERRETTA, PAUL A.: A brief technical talk. 1907. 34 p. Baltimore: Williams & Wilkins Company.

BIBLIOGRAPHICAL COMMITTEE OF BOTANICAL ABSTRACTS: A guide for collaborators in the preparation of abstracts for Botanical Abstracts. 1919. 11 p. Ithaca, New York.

BROWN, GEORGE E.: Indexing, a handbook of instruction. With a preface by E. Wyndham Hulme. 1921. 137 p. London: Grafton & Company. New York: H. W. Wilson Company.

CAIRNS, WILLIAM B.: The forms of discourse. 1896. xii + 350 p. Boston and London: Ginn & Company.

CARSON, LUELLA CLAY: Handbook of English composition. 1907. xii + 275 p. Yonkers-on-Hudson, New York: World Book Company.

---

[26] The Government Printing Office capitalizes the words *figure* and *plate* (p. 37). Many journals use Arabic numbers for figures and Roman for plates. The numbering of plates in some journals is consecutive throughout each volume. Figures in plates are sometimes numbered consecutively throughout each article. A simple method, used by some journals, is to number all figures (in text and plates) consecutively from 1 up in each article.

FULCHER, GORDON S.: Editorial service. Science, 1925, lxi, 389–391.

FULTON, MAURICE GARLAND: Expository writing. 1912. xxxviii + 555 p. New York: Macmillan Company.

GREEVER, GARLAND, AND EASLEY S. JONES: The Century handbook of writing. 1918. 228 p. New York: Century Company.

GUDGER, E. W.: On the proper wording of the titles of scientific papers. Science, 1924, lx, 13–15.

HARBARGER, S. A.: English for engineers. 1923. xiii + 266 p. New York: McGraw-Hill Book Company, Inc.

HYDE, GRANT MILNOR: Newspaper editing. 1915. 365 p. New York and London: D. Appleton and Company.

IVES, GEORGE B.: Text, type, and style. A compendium of Atlantic usage. 1921. vi + 305 p. Boston: Atlantic Monthly Press.

LIVINGSTON, B. E.: The choosing of a problem for research in plant physiology. Plant World, 1912, xv, 73–82.

MANLY, JOHN MATTHEWS, AND JOHN ARTHUR POWELL: A manual for writers. 1913. vii + 225 p. Chicago: University of Chicago Press.

MANLY, JOHN MATTHEWS, AND EDITH RICKERT. The writer's index of good form and good English. 1923. 261 p. New York: Henry Holt and Company.

MELLISH, MAUD H.: The writing of medical papers. 1922. 157 p. Philadelphia and London: W. B. Saunders Company.

ORCUTT, WILLIAM DANA: The writer's desk book. 1912. 4th ed., vi + 184 p. New York: Frederick A. Stokes Company.

PLACE, FRANK, JR.: Verify your references. New York Med. Jour., 1916, civ, 697–699.

PUBLIC PRINTER: Style manual of the Government Printing Office. 1922. viii + 224 p. Washington: Government Printing Office.

RANKIN, THOMAS E.: The method and practice of exposition. 1917. 278 p. New York: Macmillan Company.

SCHRAMM, J. R.: The abstracting and indexing of biological literature. Science, 1922, lvi, 495–501.

SYPHERD, W. O.: A handbook of English for engineers. 1913. 314 p. Chicago and New York: Scott, Foresman & Company.

VAUX, C. BOWYER: How to prepare a paper for publication. 1911. 20 p. Baltimore: Williams & Wilkins Company.

WOOD, G. M.: Suggestions to authors. 1913. 64 p. Washington: Government Printing Office.

WOOLLEY, EDWIN C.: Handbook of composition. 1907. xxi + 239 p. Boston: D. C. Heath & Company.

WOOLLEY, EDWIN C.: The mechanics of writing. 1909. xxxi + 396 p. Boston: D. C. Heath & Company.

INDEX

Sans Tache

Sans Tache

IN the "elder days of art" each artist or craftsman enjoyed the privilege of independent creation. He carried through a process of manufacture from beginning to end. The scribe of the days before the printing press was such a craftsman. So was the printer in the days before the machine process. He stood or fell, as a craftsman, by the merit or demerit of his finished product.

Modern machine production has added much to the worker's productivity and to his material welfare; but it has deprived him of the old creative distinctiveness. His work is merged in the work of the team, and lost sight of as something representing him and his personality.

Many hands and minds contribute to the manufacture of a book, in this day of specialization. There are seven distinct major processes in the making of a book: The type must first be set; by the monotype method, there are two processes, the "keyboarding" of the MS and the casting of the type from the perforated paper rolls thus produced. Formulas and other intricate work must be hand-set; then the whole brought together ("composed") in its true order, made into pages and forms. The results must be checked by proof reading at each stage. Then comes the "make-ready" and press-run and finally the binding into volumes. All of these processes, except that of binding into cloth or leather covers, are carried on under our roof.

The motto of the Waverly Press is *Sans Tache*. Our ideal is to manufacture books *"without blemish"*—worthy books, worthily printed, with worthy typography—books to which we shall be proud to attach our imprint, made by craftsmen who are willing to accept open responsibility for their work, and who are entitled to credit for creditable performance.

The printing craftsman of today is quite as much a craftsman as his predecessor. There is quite as much discrimination between poor work and good. We are of the opinion that the individuality of the worker should not be wholly lost. The members of our staff who have contributed their skill of hand and brain to this volume are:

Composing: Roland Stultz, John Flanagan, Andrew Rassa, Edward Rice, Ernest Salgado, William Fite, Benjamin Hatcher, Herbert Leitch, Ray Kauffman, Henry Shea, Arthur Baker, George Moss, Anthony Wagner, Charles Wyatt, Richard King.

Press: August Hildebrand, Fred Lucker.

Folder: Lawrence Krug, Shipley Dellinger.

Proof Room: Alice Reuter, Mary Reed, Sarah Katzin, Ruth Trieschman, Lucile Bull, Ethel Strasinger, Angeline Eifert, Audrey Tanner, Dorothy Strasinger, Lillian Gilland.

Casters: Kenneth Brown, Ernest Wann, Mahlon Robinson, Charles Aher, George Smith, Theodore Nilson, Frank Malanosky, Martin Griffen, Henry Lee.

Keyboard: Catherine Kocent, Hannah Scott.

Cutter: William Armiger.

Books for the Bacteriologist

BACTERIOLOGY $4.00

By HAROLD J. CONN and the late H. W. CONN.

The second edition of a standard text in general bacteriology, considering the history of bacteriology, microorganisms and their activities, the nonpathogenic organisms, pathogenic organisms, and an appendix on media making, characterization of bacteria, and hydrogen-ion concentration. A text used by more than seventy institutions. *Cloth 6 x 9. 449 pp.*

MANUAL OF VETERINARY
BACTERIOLOGY $5.50

By RAYMOND A. KELSER.

A new and comprehensive study of all phases of veterinary bacteriology, considering bacteria, their morphology, physiology and classification; bacteriological methods; infection and immunity; pathogenic organisms of the class schizomycetes; pathogenic fungi; the protozoa; the filterable viruses; serology; hematology; preparation of veterinary biological products; and the bacteriological examination of milk and water. *Cloth. 6 x 9. 525 pp.*

PRINCIPLES OF SOIL MICROBIOLOGY $10.00

By SELMAN A. WAKSMAN.

A complete and systematic study of the occurrence of microorganisms in the soil, their activities, and their rôle in soil processes. Part A considers occurrence and differentiation of microorganisms in the soil. Part B, isolation, identification, and cultivation of soil microorganisms. Part C, chemical activities of microorganisms. Part D, soil microbiological processes and soil fertility. An invaluable text and reference work for microbiologists. *Cloth 6 x 9. 897 pp.*

A Complete Catalog on Request

THE WILLIAMS & WILKINS COMPANY
Publishers of Scientific Books and Periodicals
BALTIMORE, U. S. A.